SOLDIER SOLDIER

THE REGIMENT FILES

SOLDIER SOLDIER

THE REGIMENT FILES

GEOFF TIBBALLS

BCA

LONDON NEW YORK SYDNEY TORONTO

Acknowledgements

The author would like to thank the following for their friendly co-operation and invaluable help in the preparation of this book: Anne Tricklebank, Deborah Waight, Fiona Connery, Nick Lockett, Barry Ledingham, Rebecca Earl, John Withers; Katy Carrington and Susanna Wadeson at Boxtree; plus the present cast of *Soldier, Soldier*.

The publishers would like to credit the following photographers for the photographs appearing on the jacket and inside the book:
John Rogers, Tony Smith, Tony Nutley, Rod Ebdon, Nicky Johnston, John Brown, Stephen Morley, Tony Russell, Joss Barratt (Hong Kong), Ken George (New Zealand), Oliver Upton (Germany), Paul Patterson (Australia).
The publishers would like to thank all those people who appear in the photographs and who have granted their permission for us to reproduce their photographs in this book: Holly Aird, Miles Anderson, William Ash, Rakie Ayola, Debra Beaumont, Duncan Bell, John Bowe, Suzanne Burden, Angela Clarke, Alexis Conran, Jack Deam, Richard Dillane, Shaun Dingwall, Sophie Dix, Simon Donald, Susannah Doyle, Tim Dutton, Ellis Fernandez, Maritoni Fernandez, Jerome Flynn, William Gaminara, Robert Glenister, Robson Green, David Groves, David Haig, Richard Hampton, Cathryn Harrison, Dorian Healy, Paterson Joseph, Melanie Kilburn, Helene Kvale, Gary Love, Angus Macfadyen, Lesley Manville, Samantha Morton, Ben Nealon, Gareth Parrington, Simon Radford, Adrian Rawlins, Gabrielle Reidy, Rosie Rowell, Colin Salmon, Dougray Scott, Mo Sesay, Tara Simpson, Rob Spendlove, Joseph Swash, Nonie Tao, Lesley Vickerage, Kal Weber, Tracey Whitwell, Marise Wipani, Denise Welch, Lia Zografou.

While every effort has been made to trace artistes featured photographically in this book, Central Independent Television plc and the publishers will be glad to make proper acknowledgement in future editions of this publication in the event that any regrettable omissions have occurred by the time of going to press.

First published in Great Britain in 1995 by Boxtree Ltd.

This edition published 1995 by BCA by arrangement with Boxtree Ltd.

CN 2781

Designed by Blackjacks
Printed and bound in Great Britain by Bath Colourbooks, Glasgow.

Soldier, Soldier is a Carlton UK Television production for ITV and is based on characters created by Lucy Gannon.

Contents

Nancy and Paddy Garvey

Nancy Thorpe was always a tomboy. While other girls played with dolls, she preferred to join the boys in a game of football at the local rec. She liked boys a lot. She had her first kiss at the age of six, from Darren Woodley outside the girls' changing rooms, and never had any shortage of male admirers. She did not excel academically, displaying no interest in either quadratic equations or the complexities of the War of Spanish Succession, although she did captain the school hockey team – a remarkable feat since her over-exuberance was once responsible for two of her team-mates ending up in casualty. She briefly toyed with the idea of a career in nursing but did not fancy the idea of being bossed around by a lot of Margaret Rutherford lookalikes. So she set her sights on the Military Police where she knew she would be surrounded by boys. But she was more interested in getting drunk with them than in any great romance – that was, until she met Paddy Garvey.

Paddy Garvey was a real handful as a boy. He comes from a large northern family and was forever getting into scrapes. More often than not it was for trivial things like scrumping apples, but as he got older there was a danger that he could easily have gone off the rails. He started hanging around in gangs, usually with older boys whom he was eager to impress. At fifteen he was a member of a gang led by eighteen-year-old tearaway Derry Monroe. The gang regularly teased a younger boy and one day chased him on to a railway line. Paddy saw a train coming and

OPPOSITE: Beneath the jovial exterior, there is a serious side to Paddy Garvey.

BELOW: Nancy Garvey was better at catching a man's eye than any lawbreakers at the start of her career.

tried to warn the boy, but Monroe continued to pursue his quarry. The boy was killed. Monroe blamed Paddy whose family were stunned by the resultant publicity. Consumed with grief, Paddy mended his ways and set out to channel his energies in a more worthwhile direction. Although bright and quick-witted, he lacked the discipline for school work and left as early as he could to join the army. He has since been up and down the ranks a few times but none of his misdemeanours have been too serious.

Corporal Nancy Thorpe enjoyed life with the Royal Military Police. It was all a bit of a laugh – and that's what Nancy liked more than anything else. The only trouble was she found it difficult to take her job too seriously. Basically, she was soft-hearted and preferred to let transgressors off with, at worst, a friendly admonishment. Invested with the powers of the Gestapo, she chose instead to behave like a benign lollipop lady. The result was that in her two years with the RMP, she had never arrested, charged or even reprimanded anyone. This had not gone unnoticed by her superiors.

Her sergeant decided it was time for a pep talk. 'Is there some sort of problem being a military policewoman, Corporal Thorpe? Look, we're not asking you to run out in the street and drag 'em in by the short and curlies, but in two years, not one charge. It's a record, Corporal Thorpe. Do you know that?'

'Is it, Sergeant?' replied Nancy, pleased with herself.

This was not the reaction he had in mind.

Despite her apparent ignorance, the message had got through. Later that day Nancy offered the heavily pregnant Joy Wilton a lift home. Joy noticed that Nancy was less chirpy than usual.

'What's the matter?' asked Joy.

'My prat of a sergeant, that's what. Stupid git, he is. I mean, I joined to sunbathe in Malta and ski in Norway. Nobody told me you'd have to be nasty to people in God's ruddy armpit.'

It was Joy's misfortune that Nancy finally chose to heed her sergeant's warning on the journey home. Nancy had been told to keep her eyes peeled for a stolen Red Cross Landrover and, spotting a likely vehicle travelling in the opposite direction, she did a swift U-turn and headed off in pursuit, totally oblivious to Joy's increasing discomfort. Putting her foot down hard, Nancy got to

> *'There's crime on them thar streets and I've got to clean it up – until 11 anyway and then I can add to it.'*
> Nancy outlining her approach to the job

within twenty yards of the Landrover. Suddenly, a coach loomed up ahead. The Landrover swerved round it to overtake. Blind to the possibility of oncoming traffic, Nancy squeezed past too. The coach driver looked on in horror, muttering something inaudible about women drivers. One of his passengers was even more startled, for the coach had been the bus of the King's Fusiliers and Tony Wilton had just seen his pregnant wife flash by. Not unreasonably, he concluded that she was being rushed to hospital, about to give birth.

Demon driver Nancy cornered the Landrover in the Ministry of

Defence depot and apprehended the thief, one Gunner Mills. As Nancy was on the point of making that first arrest, Joy went into labour. Timing had never been Joy's strong point! Mills was coerced into driving her to hospital. Nancy was all for letting him off because he had been so helpful ... until her sergeant sternly reminded her to make a charge this time. Old habits were hard to break.

Wandering through the barracks at the end of her eventful day, Nancy made an unusual discovery – a soldier up a tree. Just as it is a firefighter's lot to rescue cats from trees, so it occasionally falls to the Military Police to bring down soldiers. But this one did not want to come down. It was Lance Corporal Paddy Garvey who had climbed up there in order to retrieve a toy gun. Mellowed by a considerable quantity of alcohol, he admired the view – one which improved considerably with Nancy's arrival. He began to serenade her with an impromptu version of 'Danny Boy'.

'This is a bit silly, isn't it?' she said.

'Might be. Might not,' called Garvey from his lofty perch.

Nancy could see this was going to be hard work.

'Why don't you come down before you break your stupid neck?'

By now, Paddy was numb to any danger. 'Make me,' he shouted down, and carried on singing, slurring and smiling in equal parts. 'You look lovely, you do.'

Concluding that a compliment from a drunken soldier was better than none at all, Nancy saw the funny side and burst out laughing. It was to prove the start of a beautiful friendship.

Garvey had been drinking to forget. Along with the rest of the regiment, he had just returned from a tour of duty in Northern Ireland and had been standing just a few feet away from Sgt Pete Bramley and an RUC officer when they were shot dead by a sniper. He knew the perils of the job – they were part of the reason why he joined – but to see a mate gunned down next to him was more than he had bargained for. So, back in England, he drowned his sorrows and drank several toasts to Bramley with CSM Henwood.

> ## *'I'm the thinking man's Bruce Willis.'*
> Paddy Garvey's self-appraisal

Paddy Garvey was not exactly noted for moments of serious reflection. Blessed with the gift of the gab, he was popular with all ranks. Unlike Dave Tucker, he knew when to stop clowning around and transform himself into a reliable, conscientious and brave soldier, qualities which would soon earn him promotion to corporal. He was also highly resourceful and enjoyed putting one over on rival companies. 'D' Company, however, took their revenge on him for stealing their prized placard by stripping him naked and abandoning him on the parade ground. Despite the cold, Garvey still managed to stand to attention.

Paddy's first attempt to ask Nancy out ended in rejection but he persevered and won her round with the present of a brooch. Soon they were an item. They shared the same sense of humour and seemed made for each other. He could even talk to her about car engines and beer. Paddy realised he was in love. He thought it was something that happened to other people, not him. But Nancy was different – he had

never met a girl quite like her. He asked her to marry him, but Nancy was no pushover and enjoyed keeping him dangling on a string for a while. But with the regiment due to fly out to Hong Kong, there was a danger that she might have overdone it.

She told Donna Tucker, 'A couple of months back he was desperate to get wed and it was me doing the "let's not rush into it" routine. I made him promise not to ask me again.'

'Well, you've changed your mind,' answered Donna. 'Just tell him.'

'Oh yeah, me propose to macho man! He's gonna love that. You don't know what he's like, Donna. If I pop the question, I won't see him for dust.'

Meanwhile, Garvey was relaying his concerns to Tucker and 'Midnight' Rawlings.

'I kept on asking her and she kept saying no.'

'You know what your trouble is,' said Tucker, 'you've always courted her. It should be the other way round.'

'You're trying too hard, Corp,' added Rawlings. 'Play hard to get.'

'Yeah,' echoed Tucker in Clark Gable mode. 'Frankly my dear, I don't give a damn. Be a bit off-hand and she'll be begging you for that ring. Worked for me.'

This was scarcely a recommendation.

Nevertheless, Garvey took the advice and, on a date at a skating rink, deliberately misunderstood Nancy's efforts to steer the conversation towards marriage. This called for desperate measures. Two days later, they were sitting in a restaurant. Nancy had more on her mind than prawn balls. Suddenly, she broke off from eating.

'Paddy, will you marry me?'

Paddy had vagueness down to a fine art. 'What, here?'

It often falls to Garvey to keep Tucker out of trouble.

'No,' said Nancy with more than a hint of sarcasm, 'at the salad bar! Forget it. I just thought that if we got married before you went to Hong Kong, then we could both go.'

Paddy was gobsmacked.

'And you'd better shut your mouth', continued Nancy, 'before they re-route the Channel Tunnel.'

Dismayed at the response, she marched to the ladies' room to give him a few moments to think. It worked a treat.

'Listen Nance,' began Paddy as she returned to her seat, 'if you really want to ...'

'It was just a thought. But if you don't want to ...'

'I don't mind.'

'Oh, don't force yourself, will you!'

Paddy sensed it was time to drop the stance. 'No. I want to marry you.'

Nancy brightened. 'Yeah?'

'Yeah. Of course I do.' He stood up and threw out his arms. 'I love you, you stupid berk!'

Nancy was embarrassed in case this declaration might put other diners off their meals. 'Ssh, sit down,' she told him.

No sooner had Garvey paid the bill than he was arranging the wedding. He raced around organising everything at breakneck speed, to the dismay of Nancy who wanted to savour the occasion. If the age of romance wasn't dead, it was certainly on a life-support machine.

She told Donna, 'I feel like I've been hijacked by this big ape swinging down through the trees.'

'Sounds all right to me,' said Donna, reasoning that an orang-utan with sweaty armpits would be a marked improvement on her Dave.

But there was another more ominous cloud on the horizon. At the skating rink, Garvey had bumped into his old adversary, Derry Monroe. Derry's younger brother Jimmy had recently joined Number One Platoon and had been upset by the constant 'new boy' taunting dished out by Tucker, Rawlings and co. Derry warned that unless Garvey looked after young Jimmy, Nancy would get to hear about the death on the railway line ten years ago.

Tucker terrified Jimmy Monroe with a booby-trapped house, but it was Garvey who was hauled over the coals. He in turn took it out on Jimmy for reporting the incident. Jimmy was at his wits' end.

Nancy's wedding dress was probably a little conservative for Donna Tucker's liking. For a start, it wasn't backless.

Nancy:

'*I can't marry Paddy – I don't even know who he is.*'

Donna:

'*Yes you do. He's the big soft sod with the blue eyes.*'

Absenting himself from Garvey's stag night, Jimmy bumped into Nancy. Not knowing who she was, he told her about the sadistic Corporal Garvey and how he had once killed a lad. This was not exactly what Nancy wanted to hear about her future husband. Back at the accommodation block, Nancy found a newspaper clipping in her pigeon hole. It told how Garvey had been responsible for the death of a fifteen-year-old boy. By the time Garvey had regained consciousness after the evening's excesses, Nancy was waiting for him.

'You call yourself a corporal! You're nothing but a drunk, a wreck, a fool and a bully.'

'I am not a bully.'

'Oh no? Ask Jimmy Monroe. And it's not the first time, is it? And if you really think I'm lining up to be your next victim, you can take your special licence, Paddy Garvey, and shove it where it'll do most good.'

The next day was taken up with a live-firing exercise. Blaming Jimmy for the row with Nancy, Garvey hounded him at every opportunity. His nerves in shreds, Jimmy started to panic as gunfire flew over their heads. He tried to roll through a hedge but left his safety catch off. The gun went off and the bullet missed Garvey by a whisker. Furious, Garvey threatened to hit him. Jimmy could take no more and stuck his gun under his neck and threatened to shoot himself. Garvey realised he had gone too far. Speaking calmly and deliberately, he persuaded Jimmy to put down the gun. That accomplished, he explained the history between himself and Derry.

'Any trouble for miles, it was down to us. I was still at school. I was no good at the hard stuff. I wanted to be but ... wimp, jessie, I had the lot. So when there was someone younger than us and they all turned on him, I had to join in ...'

Garvey went on to recount how he had tried to save the boy on the railway line. It had all come back to haunt him again when he saw Jimmy putting the rifle to his chin. At that point, Major Cochrane strode towards them. Garvey covered for Jimmy, saying Jimmy had twisted his ankle.

Paddy resolved to tell Nancy the truth about the boy's death. 'I know, love, I know I should have told you but I was ashamed. I was part of it. I'm still ashamed.'

Nancy was moved. She gazed into Paddy's sad eyes. 'I wish I didn't fancy you so much.'

'Don't wish that, Nance. You make me feel like I've won the pools – every day.'

The wedding was back on.

'Impetuous, irreverent, anarchic. Unusual in a policewoman. But also perceptive, helpful and good-humoured.'

The report by Nancy's superior officer

The newlyweds settled quickly into life in Hong Kong. Nancy's star, in particular, was in the ascendancy. She was now beginning to take her career far more seriously and was put on a six-month attachment to Special Investigations Branch. One of her first assignments was vice patrol which took her to the notorious night-club-cum-brothel known as Madam Chow's.

'This place is clean,' protested the proprietress.

'This place is about as clean as a monkey's arse,' said Nancy.

As fate would have it, Nancy's raid coincided with a Tucker-inspired regimental outing to Madam Chow's. Garvey was too drunk to avail himself of any extras and Tucker managed to smuggle him out before Nancy spotted him. But when Tucker contracted VD, Nancy had to interview him and it slipped out that Garvey had been there too that night. Nancy was livid.

'I'm clean,' insisted Paddy.

'And that makes it all right, does it, you bastard? You made love to me, you bastard!'

The sudden split was painful for both Nancy and Paddy.

She slapped him round the face.

'Look Nance, nothing happened. I was unconscious. Nothing could have happened.'

'Oh bullshit! The intention was there and that's all that matters to me, pal.'

She got up to leave. Paddy tried to stop her.

'Don't touch me!' yelled Nancy. 'Don't you come anywhere near me and if you want to sleep with someone, you can try the brothel down the road.'

Harmony of sorts was restored after Nancy verified that Paddy had not slept with any of the girls, but she began to sense that they wanted different things from life. She was twenty-five and wanted a career. He was twenty-seven and wanted a family. With the future of the regiment in doubt, Paddy even considered leaving the army so that they could spend more time together but since Nancy was excited about her full-time promotion to the SIB, he decided to stay on. There seemed little point in his quitting the army if she was going to throw herself into a military career. While Paddy was in New Zealand, Nancy learned of an unexpected vacancy on a sergeant's course. It would mean at least ten weeks in the UK but could help her move right up the ladder, possibly even to a commission in time. Nancy was thrilled but said she would have to talk to her husband before accepting.

She decided to put it to him in person and flew out from Hong Kong to New Zealand. He was less than enthusiastic.

'Come on, Nance, we've got so much going for us. What do you want to spoil it for? You know what it'll mean – different ranks, separate postings. What about kids?'

Paddy tries to soothe the pain with nurse Christina Meissner.

'Let's not talk about kids now, Paddy. This is a big chance for me – I thought you'd be pleased. I want to get on.'

Over the next few days, Nancy tried to sit him down for a reasonable discussion but his mind was made up, all the more so following the tragic death of Fusilier Vinny Bowles on a live-firing exercise. Paddy used Bowles' death as emotional blackmail.

'I don't want to talk about your bloody promotion – you know how I feel. You needn't think I'm going to rubber-stamp some scheme that'll tear us apart, 'cos that's what'll happen, Nance, and you know it. Our marriage matters – it matters even more after Vinny. At least, it should do.'

Nancy returned to Hong Kong, determined to take her posting to the UK. Paddy followed in a last-ditch attempt to talk her out of it. The atmosphere between the two was understandably frosty.

'I've booked a flight for London tomorrow morning,' said Nancy.

'I see,' bristled Paddy. 'So I get back from New Zealand to find you've already gone? Is that it?'

'This is important to me. Can't you help me? I mean, I know you always expected that one day I'd see sense, settle down and become a typical army wife. Well, I can't do that. I know I was lousy at my job when we first met – all the jokes about me never making an arrest – but it's different now. I'm good at it. It's a ten-week course for God's sake. It's not a bloody lifetime. You didn't come back to talk to me – you came to stop me from doing what I want.' She tried to reassure him. 'I'm not walking out on you. I want you to support me.'

In Germany, Paddy landed in the guardhouse. At least it made a change from the doghouse.

Paddy bravely rescues the children from the nursery in Germany.

Her words fell on deaf ears.

'One poxy stripe on your arm is worth more than our marriage, is it?' blasted Paddy.

Nancy refrained from a caustic response. She stopped to think for a moment. 'We've made a right old mess of this, haven't we?' she said. 'First hurdle we come to, we fall flat on our faces.'

Paddy put his arms around her waist. 'I love you, Nancy, and I want you with me.'

Nancy broke off. 'On your terms.'

'No terms. I just want you to stay. I'm asking you to stay, Nancy. Asking you, not telling you.'

Nancy kissed him on the forehead. 'I can't, Paddy.'

Germany was a miserable period in Garvey's life. While the other lads were out enjoying themselves, he sat by the phone at night, waiting for Nancy to ring. She

'I blew it, I really blew it.'
Garvey reflecting on the split with Nancy

never did. He got by with a little help from his friends, notably Christina Meissner, the German girlfriend of Lt Giles Chapman. Encouraged by Christina's flirting, Garvey went for a drink with her in a Munster club, The Black Cat. There they noticed fifteen-year-old Sarah Stubbs, daughter of CSM Stubbs, drinking and dancing with a man. Acting in Sarah's best interests, Garvey stepped in and warned the man off before sending Sarah home in a taxi. But in doing so, he accidentally tore the sleeve of her dress. When she arrived home, she told her parents that Garvey had molested her. Chapman arrived at the club and insisted that Christina leave with him. Garvey drank on alone so

The accident in Cyprus which caused Paddy's temporary blindness.

that by the time Michael Stubbs arrived for the showdown, Garvey was too smashed to defend himself either verbally or physically.

Stubbs was under no such handicap although he was happy to let his fists do most of the talking. 'I ought to frigging kill you, Garvey. You're finished, lad.'

Garvey was too drunk and too depressed to take in the full implications. He staggered back to barracks and did what he always did in moments of despair – he climbed a tree and sang 'Danny Boy'. But there was no Nancy to serenade and that depressed him even more. He saw Chapman's flashy sports car. Suddenly all his bitterness was focused on that car. He started up a tank and drove towards the car. Wilton saw what was happening and threw himself in front of the car. Garvey stopped just in time.

Garvey was thrown in the guardhouse pending court martial. Even Christina's revelation about what really happened to Sarah Stubbs appeared unlikely to have any beneficial effect. Then while digging a ditch under Chapman's supervision, Garvey noticed to his horror that a fire had broken out in the newly established children's nursery. Remembering that gas canisters were still stored in the building, Garvey made a heroic dash to raise the alarm, just managing to get all the women and children to safety before the building exploded. He had saved the children and his career. The charges against him were dropped.

Despite this reprieve, the outlook was still gloomy. His sad domestic situation was driven home to him, first when he was forced to move out of married quarters and then, when making his will before going to Bosnia, he had to remove Nancy's name. Somehow, it seemed to make their separation final. Christina provided a degree

of comfort but Garvey was not really ready for a serious relationship with someone else. They drifted their separate ways and while he was away in Bosnia, she met and married someone else. On his return, he was awarded the Queen's Gallantry Medal for an 'act of outstanding courage while under sniper fire in Central Bosnia'. He had bravely rescued a mother and child. He was proud of the award but would gladly have forgone it if he could have had Nancy back. Any hopes in that direction were dashed when divorce papers were forwarded to him in Cyprus. He knew it was time to get on with the rest of his life.

Garvey was in line for promotion to sergeant. Another

OPPOSITE: *Paddy struggled to come to terms with losing his sight.*

ABOVE: *Receiving the Queen's Gallantry Medal, Paddy is congratulated by nephew Sam and Sally Hawkins.*

'Something's not right. I can't see anything. I can't see a bloody thing.'

Garvey after the exercise accident in Cyprus

chance to impress came with a beach-landing exercise. It very nearly wrecked his career for good. All was going smoothly until Garvey's boat struck a submerged oil drum, catapulting Tucker and Fusilier Eddie Nelson into the sea. Nelson quickly surfaced but there was no sign of Tucker beyond a floating lifejacket. Garvey dived in and managed to locate Tucker and drag him back to the boat for resuscitation. In doing so, Garvey hit his head on the side of the boat. Suddenly, he could not see. It was a panic unlike any he had ever known before. He kept opening his eyes in the hope that his sight would return. But there was nothing. Just blackness. He was told by the doctor, Major McCudden, that he had suffered a brain haemorrhage. With complete rest, his eyesight could return.

Garvey felt so useless lying there in hospital. Even the visits from his mates could not cheer him up. If anything, they made him feel worse, made him realise what he was missing out on. Tucker's bedside manner certainly left a lot to be desired.

'I just want you to know', began Tucker solemnly, 'that if what's happened doesn't get better, I'll look after you.'

'Well, that's a spur to recovery ...'

'You've got to be prepared, Paddy. You've got to look at the worst that can happen.'

'No, I don't. What are you like! It's bad enough lying here in the dark like a spare prick without you reminding me I might have to spend the rest of my life like this. I'm going to get better, Dave. Do you understand me? Now that's all I want to hear and if you don't like that, just don't bother coming to see me.'

Garvey was dying for the toilet. In the absence of the nurse, it fell to Tucker to escort him along the corridor. As they struggled along, Garvey lost his balance and crashed to the floor. He was rushed to the operating theatre. Already feeling guilty about the original accident, Tucker was now more distraught than ever. Fortunately, the fall caused no further brain damage and Garvey was soon well enough to ask his nurse, Corporal Mitchell, for a date. The setting was slightly different from the back row of the Odeon – the two chatted in his hospital room. It seemed to help. A couple of days later, his sight returned. Nurse Mitchell, who was clearly very fond of Garvey, quietly slipped away, her job completed.

Garvey's return to the regiment coincided with Tony Wilton's demotion to corporal following a fracas with an American soldier. With Wilton's blessing, Garvey successfully put himself forward for the vacant post of Platoon Sergeant. His new status as acting Sergeant brought him into contact with one of the cooks, Sergeant Sally Hawkins, a perky fitness instructor. Romance soon blossomed and, in order to have some privacy to get to know each other better, Garvey rented a flat. A visit from his brother Danny and nephew Sam made Garvey realise how much he wanted a family – he deeply regretted not having tried harder to keep Nancy. He was determined not to make the same mistakes with Sally. There would be no rushing things, no pressure upon her to move into the flat. In the end, Sally made the first move.

'I've been thinking,' she said. 'It seems daft me coming to visit all the time. If you wanted, I could spend a bit more time there.'

'You move in with me, you mean?' asked Garvey hesitantly, making sure he was not getting hold of the wrong end of the stick. 'Are you sure?'

Sally expected him to be more enthusiastic. 'Not if you don't want to.'

'I'm not saying I don't want to, Sal. It would be fabulous for us to be together like that. It's just ... well, I don't want us to rush in and spoil everything. This is important to me. You're important to me. I want everything to be right for us. I want us to know each other before we make any really big decisions.'

They agreed to give the matter a little more thought but their plans were wrecked by Tony Wilton's death on a training exercise. Confused, Garvey held himself partly responsible for the loss of his pal, for Garvey had crossed swords with the Range Warden, Norton, and had seen his cache of illegal stores, yet had not foreseen the consequences.

'I can't stop thinking about it,' he told Kate Butler. 'I know at the end I was the sergeant and Tony was the corporal but that wasn't right. If he'd been running the exercise, I don't think that accident would have happened. I was in Norton's room at the range. I saw all the gear he had. I had the chance to realise what could have happened. If I'd been awake, I would have. Tony Wilton would have been alive. It's thrown me. Really has. I mean, I know we're soldiers used to death – supposed to be. But to die like that. For what?'

It didn't work out with Sally, but just when he was beginning to give up hope of ever meeting the right girl, who should come back into his life but Nancy! The King's Own Fusiliers were posted to new barracks which just happened to be where Nancy, now a sergeant in the SIB, was based. In the course of an investigation, she found herself having to question Paddy. It was an awkward experience for both parties but there were distinct signs that the turbulent relationship between them could have a happy ending.

Dave and Donna Tucker

Dave Tucker was born in Newcastle-upon-Tyne in October 1968, the youngest of three brothers. His mother, a cleaner for British Rail, had a fiery temper and even his welder father could not fix the broken home. Their stormy marriage finally fell apart when Dave was 10 and the boy was sent away to be cared for by his paternal grandmother. Dave proved an abject failure at school (except as the class clown) but acquired a number of extra-curricular qualifications including car theft, threatening a police officer with a snooker cue and eating a vehicle licence to obstruct the course of justice. With the courage of his convictions, he joined the army as a spotty eighteen-year-old and swiftly added lateness, drunkenness and disobeying orders to his CV.

Donna Deeley also hails from a working-class background in Newcastle. Her home life was similarly troubled. Her dad has been in and out of prison and her sister Denise had an abortion at sixteen. Denise booked herself into a posh clinic and the first the rest of the family knew about it was when she could not pay the bill. School held no interest for the wayward Donna and she became a slave to night-clubs and the local fish and chip emporium. She met Dave Tucker in one such club when he was home on leave from the army. He was out for a pint or seven with his mates but was captivated by the girl sitting on the bar stool. He was not sure whether she was wearing a skirt or a large belt. When the DJ played Dire Straits' 'Romeo and Juliet', Dave whisked her on to the dance floor for a smooch. It may not have been what Shakespeare had in mind but it was effective. On his next leave, he proposed to her in a bus shelter. Before she could give her answer, their bus arrived and he had to re-enact the proposal scene on the top deck, before an appreciative audience of late-night revellers. To drunken chants of 'Give him a Y, give him an E, give him an S', Donna agreed to marry him. She sensed a kindred spirit but was unaware that in the process, she was also marrying the army. Time and money dictated a honeymoon in North Shields. And that was one of the high spots of their marriage.

The queen of fake furs, micro skirts, laddered tights and cheap sling-back stilettos, Donna is always rough and usually ready. She boasts the most occupied front this side of Bosnia. Donna is sexy and she knows it. Tucker knows it too and that is why, in spite of the fact that they fight like Tom and Jerry, he fancies her something rotten.

OPPOSITE: *Love's young nightmare – Dave and Donna Tucker.*

Tucker's dilemma has always been to ensure that Donna is not collaborating with the enemy in his absence. He has heard all the jokes – about more men going down on Donna than on the *Titanic* – but, initially anyway, attributed them to his colleagues' jealousy. But Donna became bored out of her skull being left on her own while Dave was away playing soldiers. Unlike Joy Wilton, her idea of fun was not spring-cleaning the married quarters. She wanted to bop the night away, preferably with male company. Her motto was the same as the song: 'If you can't be with the one you love, love the one you're with.'

So it was that Fusilier Dave Tucker returned early from a week's survival training in Wales to find Donna in bed with a builder

'All the men in the King's Fusiliers and she chose Tucker!'

Lt Colonel Dan Fortune eyeing Donna wiggling as she walks

named Mike. While Tucker went berserk, Donna sought refuge in the home of Colour Sergeant Ian Anderson. Tucker came to get her back.

While Tucker was away, Donna would play.

Finding his way blocked by Anderson and Paddy Garvey, he lashed out at the former and knocked the latter unconscious, before going AWOL. Inside, Donna remained utterly shameless.

'Well, what am I supposed to do while he's away,' she told the Andersons' teenage daughter Clare, 'sit and twiddle me thumbs?'

'Was he a soldier?' asked Clare, intrigued.

'Nae fear. He's got his own house, his own car. He's dead nice with it. Good in bed 'n' all.'

Tucker soon gave himself up. He was charged with committing actual bodily harm (on Garvey), disobeying an order from a superior officer (Anderson) and absenting himself from barracks. He was sent for court martial. Donna was conspicuous by her absence until Lt Nick Pasco finally persuaded her to visit Tucker in his cell. She attempted to explain.

'Look, I just went to the pub, OK? And he followed us home. I couldn't help it.'

Dave was not impressed. 'I know. You couldn't help getting into bed with him neither, I suppose?'

'We didn't do anything.'

'You're a liar!'

'We didn't, man.'

'I saw it with me own eyes.'

'Yer own eyes, my arse! You were drunk. That's all you're good for – drinking and fighting. Well, I'm buggered if I'm going to get the blame for it. I'm sick of it, I am. You in here all the time, me on me own. Nae fun and up to me neck in debts.'

'That's your fault.'

'My fault! On the poxy money you give us. At least Mike gets a decent wage ...'

This was too much for Tucker.

'You're still seeing him, aren't you?' he shrieked, leaping to his feet. He made a grab for Donna and ripped her T-shirt. The visit was terminated.

Cadman wanted Tucker discharged from the army – 'I think the man's a waste of time' – but Pasco, who had the unenviable task of defending him, began to realise just how the much the army meant to Tucker. It was just that sometimes he had a funny way of showing it.

> *'Let's face it, he's not one of our success stories, is he?'*
> Major Tom Cadman on Dave Tucker

'The army's about the only good thing that's ever happened to Tucker,' Pasco told Lt Colonel Fortune. 'I think we've got certain responsibilities.'

Tucker saw the army as his family. After a succession of dead-end jobs, it was the first he had been able to hold down. He was desperate to hang on in there. Donna did not share his enthusiasm. She hated the house and she hated the army. She wanted out. She thought Mike was an option – until she called on him after he had stood her up for a date at the Neon Colada nightclub and discovered he was married. Another bastard. Now the only hope of saving her marriage was for Dave to be kicked out of the army.

At the court martial, Tucker was sentenced to six months' military detention, after which he was free to rejoin his regiment. Donna was horrified and started packing.

'I'm not sitting here on me arse for six months while he does time,' she told Garvey, 'especially if he's staying in at the end of it.'

'When are you coming back?' asked Garvey, concerned.

'I'm not.'

Leaving Dave to read a farewell note, Donna hitched a lift and headed for Newcastle in the cab of a lorry. Back in the bosom of her bickering family, she realised that if life with Dave was hell, life without him was somehow even worse. Within a few weeks, she was back and telling Carol Anderson, 'I miss him something rotten. I must be off me sodding head.' The happy couple were reunited.

After serving his six months, Tucker was set on keeping his nose clean for a while. Apart from anything else, he felt he owed something to Fortune who had looked after him when he was a raw recruit. He even began eulogising about army life to the colonel's girlfriend, Rachel Elliot, pointing out how much better it was than the dole or working in a factory.

Rachel was stunned. 'You really are keen, aren't you?'

'Give over,' replied an embarrassed Tucker. 'Someone might hear you.' Such loose talk could have ruined his image.

When Fortune's helicopter went missing, Tucker displayed genuine concern and tried to keep Rachel's spirits up. On Fortune's safe return, she made army history by paying Tucker a compliment.

She told Fortune: 'He was kind. He was funny. He thinks the world of you.'

'So he should,' came the matter-of-fact reply. 'Anyone else would have chucked him out years ago.'

Hong Kong should have been the making of the Tuckers. New country, new start. What they had not bargained for was a new baby. Not that Dave minded in the least. He was over the proverbial moon at the prospect of becoming a dad. But for Donna, having one kid around the place – Dave – was quite enough. Not only was she scared about the physical side of giving birth, but a baby would cramp her style. It's tough going clubbing in sensible shoes and a maternity smock. So it was with some hesitation that Tucker finally broke the news to Garvey.

> *'Dave Tucker's all right. People like him. But he's a bit of a wide boy, quick, so you'll have to be quick too.'*
> Paddy Garvey to Fusilier Jimmy Monroe

'I'm going to have a baby,' he announced quietly at the door of the urinal.

Garvey sensed something was amiss and could hazard a guess at the cause. 'How's Donna taking it?'

'Oh dead pleased,' said Tucker boldly before honesty took over. 'Well ... she will be.' For a moment he was lost in his dreams. 'I never thought I'd have me own family. I've never had me own family, y'know. I wanna get me first stripe as well – y'know, start getting somewhere.'

OPPOSITE: Dave Tucker – the pride of the King's Own Fusiliers.

He had reckoned without Donna. Matters came to a head at a regiment barbecue.

'You're just made up with being a dad,' screamed Donna. 'It doesn't matter how I feel.'

'Paddy Garvey —'

'You've told Paddy Garvey! Thanks a lot!' She stormed off. 'I'm bloody terrified. I'm not having it. I'm getting rid of it.'

'You're bloody not!' shouted Dave, chasing after her.

'You watch us,' yelled Donna, defiantly.

'You do that and I'll bloody kill you!'

The padre managed to effect an uneasy truce but Tucker was too angry to remain calm for long. When he called Donna a murdering bitch, she slapped him round the face – hard.

Garvey tried to look on the bright side. 'Dave, this time tomorrow she'll be knitting romper suits, shovelling kippers and marmalade. You'll see.'

Tucker knew her better. 'Not her.'

The scene at the barbecue had done little to enhance Tucker's prospects of either father-hood or promotion. He was also in deep water with Lt Colonel Fortune after allowing two young Chinese illegal immigrants to escape. 'They were kids,' he told the padre. 'Bloody soldiers chasing after bloody kids. They looked terrified.'

Tucker's paternal concern brought him before Fortune. 'This is another court martial offence,' boomed Fortune. 'Are you going for the record?'

A more serious Donna was to emerge later.

'I was in a bit of a state, sir,' stammered Tucker. 'She's doing away with me kid. She's only twenty miles away but she might as well be in Newcastle for all I can do about it.'

Not for the first time, Fortune took pity on the hapless Tucker. 'Between now and Monday morning, sort your sodding marital affairs out.'

Donna had indeed decided to go ahead with the abortion until she saw the state of the back-street clinic. Horrified by its medieval appearance, she ran off at the last minute. It gave her time to reconsider. Working nights in a British bar – anything to relieve the monotony of being stuck in the quarters alone while Dave was on duty at the border – she was chatted up by one of her regular customers, Norm, an American from Ohio. She agreed to have dinner with him but explained that there was nothing else on the menu. Norm backed off and started to talk about about Marie, his wife back home, and how much he missed her. Donna realised that he was as homesick as her and finally began to appreciate what a great father Dave would make. She and Norm parted as friends with Donna resolved to keep the baby after all.

'You'd fall in a cesspit and come up smelling of roses.'
Donna to Dave

Hopes that impending parenthood might instil a sense of responsibility in Dave Tucker proved somewhat optimistic. No sooner had he declared his undying love for Donna than he was frequenting Madam Chow's, an establishment which dispensed pleasure and venereal disease in equal doses. An ominous itching sensation made him realise that he was infected, a situation he sought to remedy by dipping his penis in cleaning fluid. It was not one of Tucker's wiser decisions. Racked with pain, he could not even bear to make love to Donna. She wrongly attributed his sudden lack of interest to the fact that she was pregnant. Donna took umbrage. Dave took antibiotics.

It was against such an unpromising background that Tucker took part in the junior NCO cadre, hoping to earn that coveted stripe. To the amazement of everyone, he came through with flying colours and was promoted to Lance Corporal. At least Donna would have a bit more money to spend.

But the good times never last long with the Tuckers. Soon after the birth of baby Macaulay, the King's Fusiliers were posted to New Zealand. Donna was on her own again. To make matters worse, they had a blazing row the day he left – 'a real Dave and Donna special', related Garvey.

Tucker was feeling sorry for himself. He reckoned Donna had gone off him since she had had Macaulay. Worse still, the fact that she had not written to him from Hong Kong was being noticed by his mates, especially Fusilier Vinny Bowles who received more letters than Claire Rayner.

'Sod her!' snapped Tucker as the next consignment arrived.

'Wanna read one of mine?' offered Vinny.

'Go boil yer head!'

Back in Hong Kong, Donna was bemoaning her fate to anyone who would listen. Sheena Bowles was quick to sympathise.

'That's Dave all over,' pronounced Sheena, 'unfeeling, uncaring.'

Donna was mildly put out. 'Hey, that's my husband you're slagging off.'

Donna's mum, Rita, had flown out too and was babysitting Macaulay when she was not hitting the shops. She had heard all Donna's tales of loneliness before and reminded her: 'If you wanted a husband on call, you should have stuck with that bloke who delivers the pop.'

Soon, Donna got the chance to put the fizz back into her marriage when Sheena won a prize of travel vouchers as a store's one millionth customer. Aided by Nancy Garvey, Donna persuaded Sheena to use the air miles to buy the three wives flights to New Zealand.

Mum was practical to the last. 'Have you packed your backless black?' she enquired.

'Aye,' replied Donna, 'but with the black court shoes or the red slingbacks?'

'Well, if the row was as bad as you said, the slingbacks. Now's not the time for subtlety.'

Once in New Zealand, Donna wasted no time in making up.

Their latest rift healed, Tucker enjoyed himself in New Zealand, winding up the locals, until a live-firing exercise claimed the life of his pal Vinny Bowles, killed by an exploding mortar. Tucker and Tony Wilton were first on the scene. Bowles had sustained massive abdominal and throat wounds and was having great difficulty breathing. Tucker and Wilton performed a tracheotomy. They thought they'd managed to save him, but Bowles died in the helicopter on the way to hospital. Tucker was mortified.

The amalgamation of the King's Fusiliers and the Cumbrians to form the King's Own Fusiliers meant another change of scenery, this time to Munster, Germany. As far as Donna was concerned, at least it was nearer to

> *'What's your husband ever achieved apart from a court martial? He's a crap soldier, he always was and he always will be.'*
>
> A distraught Sheena Bowles to Donna

Newcastle than Hong Kong. In keeping with her husband's new status, she decided it was high time they bought a new car and set her sights on a flashy BMW convertible. In an attempt to win Dave round, she cooked him his favourite dinner. He would not budge. Dinner ended up in the bin. After conducting his own test drive, Dave relented and, to help pay for the car, Donna went for a bar job. To her horror, she found that the job was for a stripper. She stormed out in disgust. Even Donna has her dignity. She was in such a rage that her mind was less focused than usual. On the way home, she pranged the new car.

Rather like buses, crises for the Tuckers tend to come along in groups. During an exercise intended to foster goodwill with the Malverns, Tucker hospitalised one of their men with a blow from a rifle butt. He was hauled before the new Lt Colonel, Nicholas Hammond, who told him in no uncertain terms: 'I've got no room for thugs in my battalion. You let yourself down, you let the regiment down.' Tucker was busted back down to Fusilier. His rise through the ranks had been spectacularly short-lived.

But you cannot keep a good man – or Tucker – down for long, and he was soon looking for ways to impress Hammond and Major Tim Radley. His efforts caused wry amusement among his colleagues.

'Dave is thinking of skipping leave to try for the rifle team,' revealed Garvey. 'He wants to get back into Radley's good books.'

'He hasn't a prayer of making the rifle team,' said Wilton. 'The only way

Tucker tries in vain to save the life of Vinny Bowles.

he'll get back in Radley's good books is if he stays on leave all year!'

Then Tucker came up with a revolutionary plan which was brought to the attention of Hammond.

'Ah, Tucker,' began Hammond, 'Corporal Garvey tells me you've had some kind of brainstorm – something to do with camouflage.'

'Well, I was thinking, sir,' answered Tucker confidently, 'what's the point of "camming up" the vehicles when any daft idiot can see their track marks? It's a dead giveaway, sir.'

'And your idea is to cover up the tracks with leaves?'

'Got it in one, sir.'

'In the middle of summer! Well, if you want to spend your time shaking the leaves from the trees, then I'm sure the Sergeant Major can accommodate you! A bit impractical, Tucker. Still, at least your brain seems to be working – something I've seen little evidence of before.'

Tucker was also eager to spice up his love life with Donna which now owed more to Terry and June than Rhett and Scarlett. Luke Roberts offered a word or two of advice.

> *'Donna goes for small blokes she can push around.'*
> Tucker to Wilton

'You've got to brush up your technique, mate. It's foreplay. Wine her, dine her, buy her some flowers – make her feel special.'

Tucker was puzzled. 'What for? We're married.'

Nevertheless, he broke the habit of a lifetime and bought Donna some flowers. She was almost speechless.

'Who're they for?'

'You, you dozy cow.' Dave had lost none of his charm.

He took her out for a meal and booked a hotel room for the night, leaving Luke and Bernie Roberts to babysit Macaulay. Donna was dressed to kill ... slowly.

'Get those knickers off and brace yourself,' she purred. 'I'm gonna give you the time of your life.'

Dave's ardour had wilted. 'Turn the light back on, you daft mare. Luke's just phoned. Macaulay's ill. Chicken pox.'

With their debts mounting, Tucker tried to earn extra cash by helping Terry, the car salesman, to rent out black market videos. They turned out to be pornographic. Donna was not amused and burned the lot in the garden. Terry exacted revenge by repossessing the car.

In spite of all her own problems, Donna still found time to help the other wives in times of distress. She provided a shoulder for Sheena Bowles to cry on after Vinny's death and supported Bernie Roberts in the wake of her miscarriage. And when Marsha Stubbs' teenage daughter, Sarah, found herself pregnant, it was

Donna often showed her caring side to Bernie Roberts.

Donna to whom the girl turned. Wayward teenagers found a soul mate in Donna.

Tucker was still in love with the army and there was no prouder man when he was selected at random by the computer to be the first soldier to receive his United Nations beret for Bosnia. As Kieran Voce remarked: 'Who says computers don't have a sense of humour?' Before leaving for Bosnia, Tucker had to update his will and realised that he had precious little to leave Donna. He became uncharacteristically maudlin.

'Been in the army all me life, Donna. I'm still a Fusilier, I'm still flat broke. Other blokes would have done something with their lives by now but yours truly, what have I got to leave me wife and kid?'

'It's you I want,' said Donna tenderly, 'not your will or your possessions.'

He gave her a going-away present. She had wanted a sun lamp but instead was presented with an old photo album, 'so you don't forget what I look like'. It was a rare, touching moment in the hurly-burly world of the Tuckers. It did not last.

Alas, the night before leaving for Bosnia, Tucker took it into his head to sleep with a German girl he picked up in a bar. She returned to haunt him in the form of a paternity suit.

'I think you should tell your wife,' suggested Voce.

'I'd rather not,' replied Tucker. 'I like wearing me liver on the inside, sir.'

Marriage to Donna has always given Tucker plenty to think about.

For the time being, Donna was preoccupied with a fashion show at which she modelled a bridal dress with all the subtlety of a stripper. But it was only a matter of time before the news reached her ears, courtesy of Isabelle Jennings, wife of the new CO. Donna burst into tears and set fire to the love letters Dave had sent her from Bosnia. When he finally arrived home, she slapped his face and slammed the door on him.

After licking his wounds for a while, he decided that attack was the best form of defence.

'I never burnt your love letters,' he said accusingly, 'the ones you wrote when I was away and you were in the sack with that cowboy builder. Oh, and I've still got the ones you wrote when I was in the nick doing six months for a fight I got into 'cos of that bastard.'

> *'You're like a hooker's drawers – I can see right through you.'*
>
> Donna to Dave

This was one thing Donna was not going to take lying down. 'And we've been saving that little salvo up all night, have we?'

'I'll take as much shit as you like, Donna, but I'll not have you stand here making out you're fit to found a convent.'

'Oh, so we're quits?'

'Nobody's perfect.'

'I've never wanted perfect,' she shrieked. 'Since I had Macaulay, all I wanted was you.'

'You've got me!'

'Is it worth the hassle?' she responded resignedly and walked off. She headed for Munster airport, intending to fly home to Newcastle. In the clear over the paternity claim (his name had simply been first out of the hat), Tucker learned of Donna's plans and set off for the airport, hoping to talk her round. But on his way, he discovered Tony Wilton slumped in the road. He had no option but to take Wilton to hospital (where he was operated on for appendicitis) even though he knew that by doing so, he would miss Donna at the airport. So it was that Tucker returned home, gloomily anticipating an empty house. Instead, he found Donna sitting there in the darkness. She had not been able to go through with it and wanted to make a fresh start.

'I'm supposed to look like the blushing bride-to-be, not an accident in a paint factory.'

Kelly, rejecting sister Donna's offer to do her make-up

'I couldn't walk out on us, Dave. It's a mess but it's our mess.' She looked him straight in the eye: 'I don't want this mentioned, ever.'

Meanwhile, Donna had received a phone call from her eighteen-year-old sister, Kelly, who had been paid £700 compensation from the council after falling over in the street one New Year's Eve. Falling over on New Year's Eve has long been a family tradition. Kelly wanted to treat herself, Donna and Macaulay to a holiday, whereupon Donna quickly suggested Cyprus, Dave's next posting. Keen to forget Gary, her ex-boyfriend back in Newcastle, Kelly launched into a whirlwind romance with a local lad, Nicos. Donna found herself cast in the unlikely role of disapproving big sister, much to the annoyance of Kelly.

Marsha Stubbs meets double trouble in Cyprus in the shape of Donna and sister Kelly.

'I'm not daft like you,' bristled Kelly. 'I'm not going to end up saddled like you, traipsing half-way round the world after some no-hope charmer.'

Seeing much of herself in her younger sister, Donna continued her opposition. Having nearly lost Dave, who almost drowned on a beach-landing exercise in Cyprus, she did not want to risk losing Kelly too. When Kelly announced her engagement, it called for desperate measures. Donna visited Nicos and revealed that Kelly was 'wild and greedy', far removed from the picture of innocence she had painted. Nicos panicked and promptly broke off the engagement. Kelly knew who to blame.

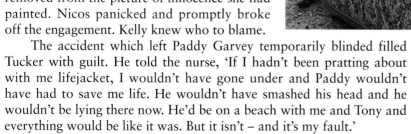

The accident which left Paddy Garvey temporarily blinded filled Tucker with guilt. He told the nurse, 'If I hadn't been pratting about with me lifejacket, I wouldn't have gone under and Paddy wouldn't have had to save me life. He wouldn't have smashed his head and he wouldn't be lying there now. He'd be on a beach with me and Tony and everything would be like it was. But it isn't – and it's my fault.'

Tucker received little sympathy from CSM Stubbs who described him as a 'walking disaster'. When the regiment returned to England to carry out ceremonial duties at Buckingham Palace, the Tower of London and Windsor Castle, he left Tucker in no doubt as to what was expected. 'You think you're the big "I am",' he barked. 'I don't. When you're on that parade square, you are not Dave Tucker, jack-the-lad. You are Fusilier Tucker, Ist Battalion King's Own Fusiliers. You're the army, you're your country, you're not some naffing turn on 'Opportunity Knocks'! You do not let us down.' Tucker got the message.

'He's got more lives than a cartoon cat.'
Lt Colonel Ian Jennings on Tucker

Donna was growing restless. Impressed by Isabelle Jennings' command of languages and knowledge of art, she started to examine her own life and did not like what she found. She felt a distinct sense of under-achievement. 'The wife of Fusilier Tucker isn't much to boast about,' she told Isabelle. 'It's just that I've never had anything other than me looks and one day I'm gonna wake up with more wrinkles than an elephant's kneecap and then what'll I do?' Isabelle's daughter Annie encouraged Donna to broaden her horizons. Donna said that she had not even been able to pass her Green Cross Code let alone learn German. It was a joke, but one which contained more than a hint of truth.

Dinner that night revolved around the same old topics.

'Ethiopia owes less money than we do,' sighed Donna.

'We should start a war,' suggested Dave, brightly. 'There might be some overtime in it.'

Tucker is rescued from drowning by Garvey and Ryan – after which Paddy was to suffer his traumatic accident.

Donna decided it was time to broach the subject of adult education, although she had a pretty good idea what the reaction would be.

'I wanna broaden me horizons,' she blurted over a mouthful of peas. 'I haven't even looked at a painting before – not a real one. Not unless it came from Woolies or had a picture of God on it. I'm gonna learn things.'

Dave was uncomfortable with education. The prospect of his wife trying to better herself made him feel insecure.

'Paintings. What next? The theatre, opera? That's not better, Donna. It's something else but it's not better.'

'What do you know?' sneered Donna. 'You never ate your chips off a plate till you met me.'

Further encouraged by Colette Daly, the girlfriend of Fusilier Farrell, Donna enrolled for a commercial studies course at the local Adult Education Institute. Walking into the wrong class-room, she was persuaded to stay by the lecturer, Mark Owens, and try out his course,

The Queen knew she was in safe hands when Tucker was posted to Windsor.

art in design. It was quickly apparent that Mark had designs on Donna. He took her to an art exhibition in Slough and afterwards invited her for a drink by the river. He kissed her but Donna made her feelings clear.

'I'm married. I want a teacher – nothing else.'

The meetings on a bench by the river continued. Donna's defences, fragile at the best of times, began to crumble.

'How long have you been divorced, Mark?' she asked.

'January 5, 1991; it made the Gulf War look like a picnic. I shouldn't joke about that, should I? Was your husband involved in all that?'

'No, he wasn't. Mind, I've had me share of sleepless nights – Bosnia, Northern Ireland – but you just have to get on with it.'

'And do you?'

Donna felt uneasy. ''Course. That's what marriage is all about, isn't it? Sticking it out ... no matter what.' She was trying hard to convince herself.

Mark persisted. 'What if it isn't circumstances that change? What if it's the people that move on?'

She looked away. 'I wouldn't know about that.'

Mark gently fingered her hair. To her despair, she enjoyed it.

Donna was late arriving home. Dave was waiting. He demanded to know where she had been. When she told him, he stormed off to confront Mark.

Mark was coolness personified. 'Any interest I take in Donna is purely professional,' he insisted. Dave thought he had made a fool of himself. But that was nothing new. In an effort to repair the damage, he bought Donna a box of paints before leaving for Kieran Voce's wedding reception. Emphasising that Dave would have to trust her in future, Donna declined to join him. Instead, she headed for Mark's house and they ended up in bed together.

A few days later, Donna arranged to meet Mark in central London. He tried to persuade her to go on the week's summer school which he was running in Brighton. She was sorely tempted.

'Dave came to see me,' revealed Mark. 'He just wanted to know what was going on. I said nothing was going on which it wasn't – then.'

Donna was horrified. 'Why didn't you tell me?'

'I know I should have but what does it matter? What happened was going to happen – eventually.'

Tucker drew the line at Donna's affair with art teacher Mark Owens.

'Was it?' screamed Donna, suddenly feeling that she was being taken for granted. She stormed off before Mark had a chance to reply.

Later, she told him she wanted to cool things. 'I want things to go back to how they were before. I want a teacher, not ... I just don't think I can handle anything more. I just don't think it's fair to other people.'

'OK, if that's what you want. But I'll miss you, Donna. I know you'll still be here, but I'll miss you.'

Mark could not let her go. He had to win her back. He phoned her and arranged to meet her in the park.

'I knew if I'd said anything about seeing Dave,' he explained, 'you'd have left that night and I wanted you to stay so much. I would have said much worse lies and I'm afraid I would again. I'm not in control here, Donna.'

'That's good to know.'

'If I seemed calculating,' he continued, 'that's not how I felt. It's not how I feel. No matter how unwise this – what we're doing – is, I want you so badly. It's all I can think about. You're all I can think about.'

'And me,' admitted Donna, touched by his honesty. 'I try ...'

This time, the invitation to the summer school was accepted.

When she told Dave of her plans, he was not a happy fusilier.

'You told me you didn't want to go,' he said.

'I know and I've changed my mind.'

'What made you change your mind?'

'Nothing. I just did.'

Dave put his foot down. 'No, you're not going – I don't want you to.'

This was red rag to a bull. 'Well, tough,' answered Donna, 'cos I am.'

Dave was becoming increasingly suspicious as to her motives. 'It's that Mark, isn't it?'

Donna brazened it out. 'No, it's not Mark. And I know you went to see him, sneaking off behind me back. You'd no right.'

'I've every bloody right! You're my bloody wife!'

Donna stood firm. 'I'm sorry, Dave. I'm doing the course. Either we trust each other and we've got a marriage or we don't.'

Donna went on her course but things simply got worse at home. Dave wanted to trust her, but could not. After all, being unfaithful was almost part of their marriage vows. He stalked around like a bear with a sore head before finally pouring out his heart to Garvey.

'A couple more days shooting people – that should cheer him up.' Tony Wilton to Joe Farrell, noticing Tucker's sombre mood on exercise

'I think she's having an affair.'

'Who with?'

'Her college tutor, Mark. I think I've been kidding myself. There's something wrong this time. We haven't had sex since she came back from summer school in Brighton. The only time she wants to be near me is when she has to be and then she can't wait to get away again. Might just be the crotch-rot and the piles,' he added, feebly trying to make a joke out of adversity, attempting to maintain his carefree image. The humour was quickly gone. 'Don't think it's that, though. I don't think it's that, Paddy.'

Garvey offered the benefit of his wisdom. 'It sounds to me like you've just got to ask her.'

'What if she says yes?'

'That's a risk you take. At least you'll know. Otherwise, you'll go bloody mad, won't you?'

Donna wanted to get things off her chest. The opportunity arose during a drunken truth game with the other wives and girlfriends. Asked to describe her most romantic moment, she quietly began: 'It was an afternoon. We slipped away from the maddening [sic!] crowd and went off on our own, just walking and talking and watching the waves. We must have walked for miles. We didn't see anybody – we just kept on going till all of a sudden it started to rain, like a real downpour. I was just wearing this little T-shirt so we slipped into this empty beach hut till it stopped. We didn't have anything with us but a bar of chocolate and a book that Mark was reading.'

'Who's Mark?' mouthed Joy Wilton to the others.

Donna was unaware of the interruption. 'He didn't need to read the poems,' she continued. 'I knew the words. I loved listening to the sound of his voice and smelling the sea, the rain. When we made love, it was just so right. And I knew I was in love with him. It was in Brighton. Mark's me tutor.'

Joy was particularly stunned and later went to reason with Donna. Having broken the ice by talking about her affair, Donna was now in full flow. She was in no mood for lectures. 'It's the most positive thing I've done for ages,' she told Joy. 'It's not just an affair any more. I love him. Mark is the first bloke I've known who wasn't just interested in getting inside yer knickers. We talk, we do things. I've never had that before. I feel like a real person when I'm with him. That's what's been wrong up till now. Nobody's ever allowed us the freedom to be meself – it's always, have you thought of Dave, have you thought of Macaulay? Well, I'm thinking of meself for once. Sorry, but that's the way it is.'

Heeding Paddy's advice, Dave tried to talk to Donna at Tony Wilton's funeral. Sensibly, she avoided him: a full-blooded Dave and Donna barney might have cast something of a shadow over the proceedings. Finally, he cornered her at home. He was determined to keep his composure, knowing that to flip would be playing into Mark's hands.

'You're having an affair?' he asked, with no more threat than an inquiry about the weather.

'No, I'm having more than an affair,' responded Donna, sitting down. 'I think I love him.'

'No, you don't.'

'I love him, Dave. I'm sorry.'

Dave's good intentions began to go out of the window. 'You don't,' he insisted, pointing at her, menacingly. 'You can't do this to me. Not now. Don't you do this to me.'

'Dave please ...'

'When did it start? Had it started that night I went round to see him? I bet it had.'

'It doesn't matter.'

'It matters to me! Had it started that night?'

'No.'

'When, then?' It dawned on him. 'That night – after that bastard sat there and denied it all.'

'I never meant it to happen. I never wanted it to – it just did.'

'You're not going! You're not going and Macaulay's not going!'

'If I wanted to leave, you couldn't stop us ...'

By now, Dave had lost control. He grabbed her by the throat. 'I can stop you taking my son. What sort of mother do you think you look like, eh? Running off and screwing your art teacher, eh? Do you think he'll want you with a kid? I doubt it. You're just a tart, Donna.

You're just a tart.' He loosened his grip. 'Go on, take my son round to that bastard's house and you see how fast he runs. Go on.'

Donna was shaken. 'It's not like that, he's a good man. He loves Macaulay ...'

She realised too late the implications of what she had said. Dave seized on the slip.

'What!' he bellowed. 'That night you had Macaulay there? You had my son? What did you do – let him watch? Or did you sit him out on the doorstep, eh?' Dave was so angry he could barely speak. 'You're not getting my son!'

He stormed out. Donna phoned Mark who came round straight-away. Just as Mark was begging Donna to go away with him, Dave arrived back, unexpectedly.

'Don't try anything,' warned Mark, more in hope than expectation.

Dave hadn't quite lost his sense of humour. 'Why, what you gonna do?' he jeered. 'You gonna paint me?' With that, he delivered a fierce blow to Mark's jaw, knocking him to the floor. In boxing terms, the artist hit the canvas. It did nothing to resolve the delicate state of affairs, but it made Dave feel better.

Donna told Joy she was moving out, not to live with Mark but to be on her own.

'Tony was just snatched away from me. Don't you throw it away.'

The widowed Joy Wilton's advice to Donna

Dave was thoroughly depressed, to the point of wishing that it had been him and not Wilton who had perished in the explosion at the training camp.

'I keep seeing that corridor in the training camp,' he told Garvey, mournfully. 'Me and Tony running down it. I wish I'd beaten him to that door. I really do.'

'Don't be bloody stupid, Dave.'

'I'm not being stupid, Paddy. I'm being right.'

'That's bollocks.' Garvey had a way with words.

'I thought about it last night,' persisted Tucker. 'It should have been my funeral and it would have read: "Here lies Dave Tucker, crap soldier." Crap. And you'd have been sad, Donna would have cried a bit, gone off with her bloke and I'd have been in heaven getting extra drill from St Peter.'

'Heaven's a bit ambitious for you, isn't it?'

'This was the one thing I got right. Marrying Donna, having Macaulay. What am I gonna do?'

Garvey placed a fortifying hand on Tucker's shoulder. 'Fight for her. Like Tony would have, like he did when he nearly lost Joy, like I never did with Nance.'

Back home, Dave made one last impassioned plea. 'I love you, Donna – more than he does, better than he does. I'm begging you, don't leave me.' The tears began to flow as he picked up Macaulay and hugged him. But it was too late. Donna was a gonna.

For the next year, they lived apart – both alone. The fling with Mark was over. The only thing that could bring Donna and Dave back together again was Macaulay.

Tony and Joy Wilton

Raised on a tough south London council estate, Tony Wilton soon learned to look after himself. What he lacked in inches, he made up for in aggression. His victims from impromptu fights staged at the local garages grudgingly admitted that he had talent and should join a boxing club. He could have been a contender. He did join a club for a while but his real ambition was to join the army. Ever since he had seen the recruitment commercials on TV, it had been the life for him: travel, action and continuing with his boxing. His mum used to joke that, even as a toddler, he marched. So, on leaving school with little more than a GCE in woodwork, he wasted no time in joining up. Tony had never really been that interested in girls. His social life revolved more around playing snooker with his mates and watching the telly. Then at a pal's party, he bumped into Joy – literally.

Joy had something of a sheltered upbringing. An only child, she lived in a middle-class suburb and, as a teenager, prided herself on having the tidiest bedroom in the area. Whereas other girls had posters of Adam Ant on their walls, Joy had a 'Keep Britain Tidy' poster and a framed photograph of Valerie Singleton. She joined the Brownies and the Guides where her organisational capabilities marked her down as a future 'Brown Owl'. At this stage in her life, male company was limited to her cousin Nigel, anorak wearer and avid bird-watcher. It was enough to put her off boys for life. Then, against her better wishes (there was a really interesting documentary about Mexican basket-weaving on BBC2), she was persuaded to go to a Saturday night birthday party at a friend's house. Joy spent the first two hours in the kitchen, supervising and generally fussing over the nibbles, before finally emerging with a tray of mushroom vol-au-vents (ones she had made earlier). In the doorway, she ran straight into Tony, seeking a refill from the party pack. The vol-au-vents went flying but, as he bent down to help her pick them up, there suddenly seemed a greater purpose to Joy's life than puff pastry. Both were shy, awkward and embarrassed at first but Tony eventually broke the ice by asking her to dance. She even took off her apron. It had to be love. Following a two-year engagement, they got married. Her parents were not keen about their daughter marrying a soldier – they had envisaged a solicitor or a nice estate agent – but when they saw how much she loved Tony, they backed down and gave their blessing. Tony may not always have had

the life the army described in its brochures, but he certainly landed the archetypal army wife.

Tony Wilton used to eat, breathe and sleep the army. His regular weekly reading was *Combat* magazine and nobody would have been surprised had he slept in camouflage gear. A walking recruitment poster, he was a dedicated professional who believed in discipline and doing everything by the book. This frequently put his friendship with Tucker under considerable strain. Wilton was not one for turning a blind eye, even where mates were concerned. He could have a fiery temper but he usually channelled it into the boxing ring where he was the regiment's welterweight champion. He loved Joy deeply and nick-named her 'pumpkin'. It was meant as a term of endearment.

Joy was intensely proud of her little tin soldier. Each week, she would brush and press his no. 1 uniform, creating a perfect network of creases which would have done credit to 'Come Dancing', let alone the army. She was as devoted to the role of army wife as he was to being a soldier. The other wives used to joke that the two of them marched everywhere in step, even to the supermarket. She was also fanatically houseproud to the point of neurosis. Their married quarters were kept spotless. You would rather eat a meal off the Wiltons' floor than the Tuckers' table. Indeed, Joy was never happier than with a can of Mr Sheen in her hand. She had a tendency to take things too seriously and it took a lot of encouragement before she would let her hair down. Even then, it was only a notch or two. She did not want to do anything that might embarrass her Tone. She did have a sense of humour but it was well camouflaged.

With a new baby, Matthew, Joy felt particularly protective and had to remind Tony that he had responsibilities towards her and the baby

Tony Wilton called his moustache his 'fourth stripe'.

as well as the army. Her mother was staying with them at the time and the two women ganged up to pour cold water on Tony's plans to fight in the inter-company boxing championships. Tony could not let the company down even though facing George Foreman in the ring was arguably less daunting than going three rounds with Joy's mum. Ultimately, Joy realised she was being unfair on Tony – a dutiful wife should not upset her husband before a big fight – and went to lend her support. It was in vain. Tony was knocked out but was cheered up by the news that Joy's mum was leaving the next day.

'I know I'm just one big joke. I just get fed up with it all the time.'

Joy bemoaning the fact that the other wives never took her seriously

To underline his commitment to the family, Tony went on a sergeants' course. By the time the King's Fusiliers left for Hong Kong, he was a fully-fledged sergeant and had grown a moustache which he referred to as his fourth stripe. Joy was at her fussiest just before the departure for Hong Kong. A born organiser, she had insisted on arranging the flowers for Nancy's wedding. When Nancy was having second thoughts about getting married, Joy's main concern was having to cancel the flowers.

Nancy rounded on her. 'I tell you what, Joy, if you can't cancel the flowers, I'll get married. OK? To keep you happy, I will commit myself to a life of misery just as long as you shut your hole about the bloody gypsophila and the daisies.'

The irony was lost on Joy: 'I couldn't get daisies.'

However, she came into her own when Paddy Garvey's stag night spilled over to the Tuckers', leaving their married quarter in an even worse state than usual. Donna was due to be 'marched out' a few hours later prior to leaving for Hong Kong – an official inspection which would fine every stain and mark in her flat. There was only one thing for it. Joy had to roll up her sleeves and transform the place into a show house. She was in her element. Such was her efficiency that the Tuckers' quarter was triumphantly passed by the accommodation officer. Donna had escaped a hefty fine.

At first, Joy found it difficult to adjust to life in Hong Kong. Matthew reacted badly to the heat and Joy reacted badly to the presence of her live-in Filipino maid, Mila. She also felt homesick and lonely, Tony being preoccupied with creating a favourable impression with his new commander, Lt Alex Pereira. When Mila tried to give Matthew some unfamiliar Eastern medicine, Joy flew into a panic and slapped her. Mila ran off and locked herself in her flat. With Rachel Fortune acting as mediator, Joy eventually patched things up with Mila. She learned that Mila had three children of her own back in the Phillipines and realised that Mila was equally homesick. Also, the magic medicine made Matthew much better. To get out of the house more, Joy contemplated a job at a Chinese kindergarten.

Tony was having his problems too. He and Pereira did not see eye to eye. Anxious to make his mark, Pereira had insisted on subjecting the men to an arduous route march, against Wilton's advice. When 'Midnight' Rawlings was taken ill, Wilton blamed Pereira. The bad feeling between the two men came to a head at Wilton's birthday party. Wilton got drunk and ended up hitting Pereira, albeit accidentally. Joy was mortified. She was convinced that he would be demoted and sent back to the UK, and that her hopes of seeing him climb the regimental ladder would be dashed forever.

'He said he'd take me all over the world,' she sobbed to Nancy and Donna. 'I just didn't think he'd take me back home again so quick! Just when it was all coming right. Chance for me to get a job, whole place to explore, then that prat goes and wrecks it all!'

In Joy's eyes, her Tone's halo had well and truly slipped. Fortunately, Pereira covered up the whole affair, Tony was not sent home and Joy got to take her job at the kindergarten. But Tony was soon in the doghouse again when he gambled away the money reserved for a new leather sofa by betting on a kick-boxing fight. Luckily for him, he won a set of golf clubs in a raffle and was able to lay them down as part payment and stop the sofa from being repossessed. Joy was temporarily appeased.

It fell to Joy to organise a special wives' club weekend in Hong Kong. It was arranged with military precision, complete with an itinerary (which had to be strictly adhered to) for the two days. Her bossiness began to irritate everyone. She acted hurt.

'Look,' she announced, 'someone's got to organise this thing properly. I mean, if someone else wants to do it, fine.'

'Give over, Joy,' said Nancy, 'there isn't anyone else – not daft enough anyway!'

Joy pressed ahead and in her opening speech, declared that the wives were representing the men.

Wilton's affair with barmaid Ellie in New Zealand was to end after it started to affect his relationship with his friends – and his promotion prospects.

'Great!' exclaimed Donna. 'We can piss out the windows and puke in the plant pots!'

It was not exactly what Joy had in mind.

The weekend had all the makings of an unmitigated disaster. Joy had organised a dreary cultural evening to see a mime artist. If he did not get his kit off, he was of no interest to Donna! Yawns were being stifled, sometimes none too subtly, until half-way through the performance, the heavily pregnant Donna led a rebellion. She feigned an attack of food poisoning and all the wives dutifully trooped out of the theatre after her. Once outside, she made a miraculous recovery and led the girls to the nearest nightclub. Joy accepted defeat with good grace and, to the amusement of the others, drunkenly chatted up some local men in the nightclub. So she was human after all.

'Your private life's your own – provided it remains private. But if your behaviour is undermining your authority as a senior NCO, that's a different matter. We want NCOs who reflect a mature authority in whom soldiers and families can place their trust and whom they can respect.'

Kieran Voce warning Wilton of the possible consequences of his affair in New Zealand

Much as he loved little Matthew, Tony was happy to escape to New Zealand for a while. He found it easier to order around grown men than look after a toddler for a few hours. He was nobody's idea of a 'new man'. One night, Wilton and the rest of the lads visited a local bar in New Zealand, the Hot Lava Club, where he started chatting up the barmaid, Ellie. When a New Zealand soldier, Milburn, started making a nuisance of himself, Wilton sprang to Ellie's rescue and walked her home. Although he insisted his motives were innocent, none of his mates believed him and they warned him not to get involved. But Wilton was too smitten to back out and the friendship rapidly developed into an affair. Joy was too busy to come out to New Zealand with the rest of the wives but baked a special cake for them to take to Tony. Made from 'an old butter recipe with excellent keeping qualities' so that it would not go stale on the flight, it was iced with the words 'I LOVE YOU'. Nancy and Donna presented it to Tony at the Hot Lava Club ... but in order to say thank you, he first had to extricate his tongue from Ellie's throat.

'I've got a present for you,' stormed Donna. 'From your wife!'

Ostracised by his friends, Wilton was also warned that his private life could affect his prospects of making Colour Sergeant. He was a man alone, his only confidante being his barmaid. He did not even love her really – she was just easy to talk to, a bit of fun. As affairs go, it was relatively innocent. Both knew it would end before long. It was Vinny Bowles' death which brought Wilton to his senses. He realised how much he needed his family and the companionship of his fellow soldiers. So he told Ellie it was all over.

'I've been thinking about my kid without a father,' he told her quietly. 'Just lately I've been losing it a bit – my sense of what's right. In the army, it's important. My mates have been shutting me out. I need to belong; I can't live out on a limb.'

Ellie was philosophical. 'There's plenty more fish in the sea. Don't expect me to beg you to stay.'

Tony fished for one last compliment. 'Did I make you happy?'

Ellie rejected the bait. 'Not really ... but I enjoyed myself.'

Tony's main concern now was to stop Joy from ever finding out. His cover was blown in Germany when the Tuckers locked horns over buying a new car. At the height of the row, with the volume up to full, Dave yelled that the only reason Tony was buying Joy a new car was because he felt guilty about the affair he had had in New Zealand. Joy happened to be outside talking to Bernie Roberts.

At first, she gave Tony the silent treatment. He knew something was wrong but his suspicions were not confirmed until the wives' club's

> *'Joy likes the attention. He's a nice fella but that doesn't mean she fancies him. If you make a big fuss, it'll only make things worse.'*
> Donna advising Tony not to become jealous of Kurt, Joy's aikido instructor

weekend exercise. Joy decided to maximise the impact of her outburst by conducting it with a loaded rifle in her hands.

'I should've blown your bloody balls off!' she told him. 'I could humiliate you the way you've humiliated me. You weren't even gonna tell me, were you? You didn't even have the guts to do that. I had to have everyone talking about it behind my back.'

Tony felt suitably small.

Joy threw herself into her new hobby, aikido, and Donna teased her that the instructor, Kurt, fancied her. He certainly seemed to be paying her undue attention. At one point, he started pontificating to Joy about spiritual strength.

Donna was not impressed. 'Haway an' shite, will yer man!'

Kurt required a translator. 'Excuse me ... ?'

'It's an old Geordie saying,' explained Donna. 'It means we've got the shopping to do, the kids to collect, the supper to be ready on the table before our husbands come back. Isn't that right, Joy?'

Despite Donna's assurances to the contrary, Tony became convinced that Joy was having an affair with Kurt. He sought a confrontation but had reckoned without Kurt's martial arts skills and finished up flat on the floor. Joy was touched that Tony had fought for her.

'Just a poor little baby, aren't you?' she said, patching up his wounds.

'He took me a bit by surprise, that's all,' replied Tony, his pride hurt.

'Still took him on though, didn't you?'

'I love you, don't I?'

'Do you?' beamed Joy.

''Course I do.' They kissed. But then Tony undid all the good work. 'We're quits now.'

Joy bridled. 'Quits! Quits for New Zealand? Tony, is that how your mind works? If you think my going to aikido is the same as that ...'

'I just thought you were trying to punish me, that's all.'

'Well, what you thought's your problem, isn't it?'

Gradually, things in the Wilton household returned to normal, to the extent that, after Bosnia, they decided to try for another baby as company for four-year-old Matthew. Tony was thirty by then and saw an addition to the family as the perfect way to mark the forthcoming promotion which he considered to be inevitable. So it was with great confidence that he marched into his meeting with the new CO, Lt Colonel Ian Jennings, only to be informed that he had been turned down for promotion to Colour Sergeant in favour of more experienced candidates.

His world had collapsed around him. 'Maybe', he told Garvey bitterly, 'I should get a tattoo on me forehead, saying "Not quite up to it."' At least it would have been a partner for the 'Royal Tournament 1980' tattoo he had had done on his bum in Amsterdam.

Joy hid her disappointment but Tony was inconsolable. He saw no future with the regular army. 'I want you both to be proud of me, Joy. I've got to move forward. I'm going to apply for the SAS.'

Joy was appalled at the prospect. 'Don't be daft.'

'I'm not being daft. I need a fresh challenge. I've got to get stuck in. The reason I'm not getting on is 'cos I've been standing still for too long. I need the sharp end of the army.'

Joy's loyalty was strained beyond breaking point. 'I don't want you going to places I don't know the name of, doing things you can't tell me about.'

Later, she aired her fears to Donna: 'SAS men disappear for months, sometimes for good.' There was a thought. Perhaps Dave could join ...

When Wilton collapsed with appendicitis during a training run, the unlikely figure of Dave Tucker sprang to the rescue.

Wilton took out his frustration on the men, particularly newcomer Eddie Nelson whom he bullied during swimming training for Cyprus. Wilton told Garvey: 'I don't need two incompetents like Tucker and Nelson blotting my copybook.' He could be all heart.

He embarked on a rigorous training schedule to prepare for his bid to enter the SAS but was not quite up to it and collapsed with appendicitis on an eight-mile run. The 'incompetent' Tucker found him and rushed him to hospital. There, Joy revealed that she was pregnant: she had been afraid

'I never thought I'd hear myself say this, but there are some things which are so much more important than the British Army. I don't give a toss about me – just so long as Joy and the kids are all right.'
Tony Wilton

to tell him because he had been so obsessed with the SAS and she was frightened the news might upset him. Overjoyed at the news, Tony immediately abandoned his plans to join the SAS.

When the men returned to Germany, Wilton took an instant dislike to a platoon of American soldiers who had arrived at the barracks on an exchange visit. He thought one of their number, Gallagher, was showing an unhealthy interest in Joy. Gallagher and another American soldier, Mather, had a bet as to who was the better driver and a slalom course was laid out at the rear of the barracks. As Gallagher was roaring around the course, his vehicle suffered a blowout and ploughed straight into Joy's car. Joy was taken to hospital but fortunately had suffered nothing more than whiplash while Matthew, who was in the baby seat, appeared to be unharmed. But there were fears for the safety of the unborn baby. When Tony found out what had happened, he hit the roof. At the hospital, he came face to face with Gallagher in the toilets. Gallagher, who had been treated for cuts and bruises, tried to apologise and offered to pay for damage to the car but Wilton was too angry to listen.

Tone was reduced in rank after thumping Gallagher, an American serviceman who crashed into Joy's car.

He started thumping Gallagher who was still too shaken by the crash to offer any resistance. 'You Yanks,' screamed Wilton, pummelling him to the ground, 'you think you own the world, don't you? You think you can buy anything!' He hauled the stricken Gallagher up from the floor. 'Think you can buy my wife? You can't buy my wife!' He dragged Gallagher over to the cubicle. 'You're nothing but a piece of shit! You know what I do with shit? I flush it down the toilet.' With that, he shoved Gallagher's head in the toilet.

The RMPs were called in and Wilton was arrested. He took full responsibility for his actions. 'I wanted to beat the shit out of him. I wanted to make him feel how I felt.'

Wilton did not need telling that he was in big trouble. He was sent for court martial and placed under house arrest. The two Americans were sent home in disgrace but not before, by way of apology, they had left Mather's prized baseball mitt and bat as a present for young Matthew. The good news was that Joy had not lost the baby.

Tony had managed to keep the whole thing from Joy while she was in hospital but on her return home, he told her all about the fight and its possible repercussions.

'I might not come back from this one, Joy. They're thinking about banging me up in Colchester nick.'

Joy could not take it in. 'You can't go to prison. We're having a baby, Tone.'

Wilton was defended at the court martial by Voce who made a sterling plea of mitigation, but the ruling was that Wilton be reduced in rank to corporal. Joy did not know whether to be shocked, or relieved that the punishment was not more severe. At least he would be around for the birth of the baby. That night, the Wiltons bravely attended a party in the NAAFI to mark the end of the regiment's stay in Germany. Few thought they would turn up but when they walked in, they received a spontaneous round of applause.

Wilton was touched by the support but it was not long before his spirits sank. He had already shaved off his moustache – his fourth stripe – and started drinking heavily. Joy began worrying about money now that he was on a lower salary. That only made him feel worse. His bitterness surfaced in a furious outburst.

'Now I'm busted down to corporal, I should pretend that I can't afford to enjoy myself anymore. I should sit here every night, lying here right in front of the telly – if we can afford a telly, that is – and waste me life away. That'd satisfy you, would it?'

Joy did not deserve this.

Money was so tight that Tony reluctantly agreed to sell the family car. They wanted to convert the spare room into a nursery for the new baby but did not even have enough cash for a couple of tins of paint – until Joy

'It's not his fault. It's just that every time I look at him, I think to myself that should be me up there. That should be me.'

Wilton revealing to Joe Farrell his true feelings about Garvey's temporary promotion to Sergeant

produced some money she had been saving for just such an emergency. And what did Tony do? He lost the lot in a poker game at the pub. Joy threw a wobbly.

'You promised me in Hong Kong that you wouldn't gamble again,' she raged. 'Get out! Get out of my house! Get out! Just grow up or I'm going to leave you. Me and the kids would be better off without you.'

Joy stayed with friends that night.

Her attempts to sell the car hit something of a stumbling block. A young man responded to her advert in the local paper and liked the car so much that he drove off in it on the spot – without paying. Garvey advised her that the chances of recovery were slim. Joy felt stupid and could not bring herself to mention the stolen car to Tony. He apologised to her for his recent behaviour and they were reunited by the birth of baby Lauren, Joy having been rushed to hospital in an old Second World War ambulance that was part of the D-Day commemorative event. Joy finally plucked up the courage to tell him about the car but he was too engrossed with his new daughter to care. Mother and baby returned home to find that Tony had redecorated the spare room overnight. Little Lauren had a beautiful nursery.

Joy was keen to show off the new baby and took her along to the barracks for a charity five-a-side football match in which Tony was playing. Joy sat in a temporary grandstand and left Lauren in her pram nearby. She was no more than fifteen feet away. With Tony about to take a penalty, Joy went to fetch Lauren so that she could see her dad become a hero. The pram was empty. Joy looked around in disbelief. She paced up and down, frantically tugging at her hair, in a state of total panic. Her throat was too dry to make a sound. And everybody else, oblivious to her plight, just sat basking in the sunshine, watching the match, without a care in the world. The silence seemed to last minutes but was really no more than a matter of seconds. Then she finally summoned the energy from within to release the cry that her baby was missing.

Tony raced across to her aid. She was surrounded by worried friends. The camp was sealed off and searched but there was no sign of Lauren. The police were called in.

Joy was hysterical. 'I mean, who'd take a baby?' she sobbed to Tony. 'Who'd want to take a baby?' Her mind flashed back to the Jamie Bulger tragedy. 'I mean, what if it's kids?' She was filled with guilt. 'I know I shouldn't have left her. I thought it would be all right, you know. I kept on checking on her, Tone. I wouldn't just leave her like that, would I? I mean, supposing it's kids ...'

The sentence did not bear finishing.

Nobody was blaming Joy but Tony soon felt that he was under suspicion. The police kept asking him whether he had really wanted the baby.

Tony deeply resented the implication. 'Let me get this straight. You think I've done something to my kid? You think I've harmed her in some way? That's sick. You're sick. Now piss off out my house!'

As the search continued, Wilton opened his heart to Garvey. 'People keep expecting me to go mad, to crack up or something. I just feel weird. I mean, I'm devastated but I can't cry. My mouth keeps going dry. I couldn't bear it – taking her to the church in a little white shoe-box. I couldn't bear it. She's so precious.'

Wilton, Garvey and Tucker face the flames outside Range-Warden Norton's storeroom. It was a training exercise which was to end tragically.

Joy took her mind off things by baking a cake.

The Wiltons' ordeal lasted some six hours. Then that evening, Lauren was found safe and well in Sarah Stubbs' bedroom. Joy would never let her out of her sight again.

After the sticky patch they had been through, the agony of nearly losing Lauren had brought Tony and Joy closer together again. They realised how much they meant to each other. Not that Tony stopped eyeing up pretty girls such as Colette Daly's blonde friend Cheryl. Joy was irritated by the way Tony fawned all over Cheryl at supper and briefly decided to dye her own hair blonde.

Tony's reaction was simple. 'Why?'

'Because', replied Joy, 'I felt like being more than just a wife and mother, someone to wait on you hand and foot. It's true, you know, all the looks you get, all the whistles, still I'll just have to learn to cope with that, won't I?'

Tragically, Tony was not around much longer to find out. The men were taking part in an NCO cadre at an army training ground near London. The range warden in charge of the training ground was Norton, an abrasive individual who was Michael Stubbs' old RSM in the Cumbrians many years back. Bitter and twisted, Norton was now a drunk and had a cache of illegal stores hidden in his den at the FIBUA (Fighting in a Built-Up Area) building. This building was an integral part of the exercise. Tony was particularly eager to impress during the exercise, hoping that he might win back his stripe. As he and Tucker made their way into the building without being captured, Tucker spotted Norton heading towards his room with a fire extinguisher. Smoke was issuing from around the door. Wilton shouted a warning and raced along the corridor but could not prevent Norton from opening the door. As he did so, there was a fireball explosion, engulfing Norton and Wilton in flames. Both men were killed. Garvey and Tucker could only look on helplessly.

As the men tried to come to terms with Wilton's death, the cause of the explosion was revealed. An electrical fault had combined with Norton's illicit stores to form a deadly cocktail. Kate Butler was given the task of informing Joy.

The wives were enjoying a party at Joy's flat. Kate entered ashen-faced. It was immediately apparent that something awful had happened. It was the moment they had all dreaded. The only question was, whose husband was it?

'There's been an accident on the exercise field.' Kate's eyes fixed on Joy. 'It's Tony.'

'Is he hurt?' gabbled Joy. 'Is it bad?'

'It's worse than that. Tony's been killed.'

'No, he can't have,' said Joy. 'Not Tone. Not my Tone.'

Joy performed stoically in adversity. She behaved with great dignity and courage at the funeral service where she read Tony's favourite war poem. It was only afterwards, when alone and finding some of Tony's socks and shirts in the laundry basket, that she allowed her grief to break through. She went and stayed with her mum for a year before beginning the painful process of trying to rebuild her life, a life without Tone.

Ian and Carol Anderson

SOLDIER SOLDIER SOLDIER SOLDIER

As a youngster, Ian Anderson was something of a loner. Whereas his brother Graham was always out playing football, Ian usually had his head in a book. Quiet and introspective, he enjoyed going out for long walks in the countryside around their home in Burnley, Lancashire, just taking in the Pennine scenery. His teachers expected great things of him, as did his parents. The pressure proved too great and he did badly in his exams. He had little option but to leave school at sixteen, drifting into a succession of menial jobs: labourer, roadsweeper, worker in a hairnet factory (where he was the only man among 150 women and was just grateful to get out alive). None of these jobs lasted more than a month. Despairing of his future, he decided to re-sit his exams at college. This time he fared much better and was ready to tackle the outside world. He found work as a management trainee with a leading high-street store and became engaged to Julie Ryman. Things seemed to be looking up. Then he was made redundant and Julie broke off the engagement – all in the space of a week. Fortunately, Carol Martin was on hand to pick up the pieces.

Carol was a soldier's daughter. She had travelled the world in her father's shadow: Canada, Germany, Cyprus, Catterick. Sensible and organised, she left school and worked in a bank. One day, Ian, touring North Yorkshire to recover from his double blow, called in to cash a cheque. He was instantly smitten – so much so that for the rest of the week, he kept on cashing cheques. Love was an expensive business. For the next three months, they conducted a trans-Pennine romance until they worked out that it would be cheaper to get married. Ian was still on the lookout for a career and it was Carol who suggested the army. It was not something he had really considered before, but the idea steadily began to appeal and in 1976, the same year that their daughter Clare was born, Ian joined up.

Carol Anderson became a stoical army wife (just like her mother). She was always ready to help new wives settle in and had a new arrival of her own in 1983 when she gave birth to son James. Ian, however, was still not convinced that the army was the life for him. He tried to broaden his horizons by doing an Open University course and studied Russian and Arabic. He was also a devotee of church architecture. In periods of doubt, it was Carol who kept him in the army. By 1991, he had reached the rank of colour sergeant, but it was widely felt that he lacked the personality and drive to scale greater heights.

The Andersons' marriage was steady rather than exciting. They only ever made love with the lights off. Although she knew it was her duty never to complain, Carol sometimes felt taken for granted. She was only too aware that if she went out and had her hair done, the last person to notice would be her husband. Ian could be cold and aloof but he doted on the children. In return, James was proud of the fact that his dad was in the army. But Clare detested every aspect of military life.

'I'd swap her for a Rottweiler if I were you.' Donna Tucker giving Carol her assessment of the rebellious Clare

With Ian about to return from the tour of duty in Northern Ireland, where Bramley was killed, Clare found it difficult to come to terms with her feelings.

Tearfully, she told her mum: 'When Mandy's dad was shot, I thought my dad would be next. I felt really bad like I was going to make it happen but I couldn't. I didn't even say I was sorry. I want to tell him I love him but we really get on each other's wick. In a couple of days, he'll be yelling at me to keep the noise down because he's doing his naff Open University, and I'll be yelling at him, and I'll never tell him. Never.'

No sooner was Ian home than an old foot injury threatened his participation in the patrol competition against 'D' Company and indeed his whole army career. Carol said he should report the injury before he made things worse.

'For God's sake, Ian, you're stuck behind a desk anyway. What does it matter if you can't leap around an assault course like a nineteen-year-old?'

'If it was the flaming Gulf it would matter, wouldn't it?' he stormed.

'You broke that foot months ago. They've not chucked you out yet.'

'Because they don't know it's giving me trouble again, do they?' He showed her the swelling. 'See. They take one look and hand me me papers.'

Carol thought even that would be better than risk damaging the foot permanently. 'Ian, there are other jobs you know.'

Ian was unimpressed. 'Security guard on a building site? Prison officer? No thank you.' Besides, he said, he could not let Major Cadman down.

Carol had heard enough. 'OK, cripple yourself!'

Ian's foot did prove a considerable handicap on the exercise but, by lying low and playing Scrabble with the Padre, he managed to remain undetected by 'D' Company. Just when Cadman was convinced that Anderson had been captured, Ian limped home to a hero's welcome.

However, Cadman did tell him to get his foot sorted out and to come to him next time he had a problem. Ian had learnt a painful lesson.

The reward for Ian Anderson's studies came when he heard that he was to be promoted to lieutenant in Intelligence. His family was less than enthusiastic. Clare was worried that she would lose any remaining street cred by becoming an officer's brat while Carol did not want to lose touch with people like the Wiltons. The situation nearly did not arise. At the stores, of which Ian was in charge, essential items of equipment went missing, including two night sights. The finger pointed at Ian, especially since he had recently lashed out on a new car. His commission was in grave jeopardy.

'They won't make you up now, will they?' asked Carol. 'I mean, if I'd told everyone ... what would they all say?'

'For God's sake, Carol! Every storeman in the regiment's going to have his records torn to pieces. Thousands missing. And it's all down to me! I've got better things to worry about than barrack gossip.'

'Perhaps it's for the best,' said Carol, seeking a crumb of comfort. 'Perhaps we're not cut out for it.'

Ian would not be pacified. 'I'm not giving up that easily. Some thieving bastard goes through my stores and you expect me to jack the whole thing in!'

When Carol and Donna set off to visit Tucker in prison, two men saw the opportunity to sneak into the Andersons' house and plant incriminating evidence. As luck would have it, Donna had forgotten her keys and the women returned to disturb the thieves. Ian put two and two together and made the connection with his colleague at the stores, Marshall. The latter confessed and implicated an ex-soldier named Hart, a friend of Major Cadman's. Ian's commission was safe and was celebrated in some style at a special Fifties party.

Four years on, Ian is still revelling in his new job. Clare is at university studying sociology and Carol is taking a business studies course with a view to returning to work when James is older. As for James, he wants to be a soldier, just like his dad.

OPPOSITE: One for the album. Colour Sergeant Ian Anderson and family.

'Wait till I tell my Dave you might be in the next cell to him ... only joking!'

House-guest Donna Tucker when Ian Anderson faced an accusation of theft

Kate Butler

If anybody appeared to come from good officer stock, it was Kate Butler. But appearances can be deceptive. The only military blood in her came from being bitten by a regimental goat while watching the Trooping of the Colour. Her parents met at a Beatles concert. Her dad was a roadie and threw out her mum who had climbed in through a window, hoping to see the Fab Four. Five years later, in 1969, Kate was born. She was educated at a secondary modern school in Catford, south London, where she emerged as a copybook all-rounder. The holder of a Duke of Edinburgh's Award Scheme Gold, she hit upon a future in the army since it was the one career which would enable her to indulge all her outdoor and adventure training interests as well as offering a sound career structure. So, after passing her 'A' Levels, she went to Sandhurst.

Kate Butler came a long way from Catford Secondary Modern.

She was posted to Kuwait during the Gulf War and joined the King's Fusiliers as Assistant Adjutant, just prior to their posting to Hong Kong. An excellent rock-climber, swimmer, pot-holer, hang-glider and water-skier, as an action girl Lt Butler made Anneka Rice look like Judith Chalmers. She quickly earned the grudging respect of Garvey after proving herself to be the superior climber on the dash to rescue Fortune from his helicopter crash. Later, Garvey covered up for her when she made an uncharacteristic map-reading error. They were equal now and developed a good, solid professional relationship which even touched on friendship. When Garvey was desperate to flee New Zealand to see Nancy in Hong Kong in a bid to repair his marriage, it was Kate who arranged his leave and even lent him some money.

Kate was wary about becoming involved with men at work. As the only woman in the regiment, she was aware of the widespread interest in her 'bedability' but did not wish to compromise her position. In Hong Kong, the handsome Lt Alex Pereira made a play for her but she resisted at first, saying that she wanted to be taken seriously, not to come down to breakfast to a chorus of sniggers. Even the offer of a

Kate's abilities as a soldier soon earned the respect of Garvey and they became firm friends, particularly when Garvey sought her advice over his split with Nancy.

'It's hard enough living in the mess with all the guys. I've just about got things so I don't have to padlock my bedroom door every night.'

Kate explaining to Alex Pereira her reluctance to enter into a relationship with him

plate of noodles failed to tempt her. But Pereira would not take no for an answer.

'I'll wear a funny nose and false moustache,' he suggested.

Kate saw the joke and gave in.

They went out on their date and were hugely attracted to each other but Pereira had already been subjected to good-natured ribbing from the men. He thought it only fair to tell Kate.

'What you were saying yesterday, about being taken seriously, you were right, you know.'

'Why?'

Pereira took a deep breath. 'The whole platoon seems to think we're ... doing it.'

Although the idea was by no means repugnant, it confirmed Kate's worst fears. 'Oh God!' she exclaimed and turned to gaze at the Hong Kong skyline by night.

'Wait!' said Pereira. They kissed passionately before he broke off to say: 'I think you're right. I think it would be more difficult for you than it would be for

ABOVE: Romance with Alex Pereira in Hong Kong was doomed to failure.

OPPOSITE: Kate had better luck with the dashing Keiran Voce.

> *'She's all work and no play, that girl. If I was cooped up with 600 members of the opposite sex, I'd have a lot more fun than she does.'*
> Dave Tucker's view of Kate Butler

me.' This speech was hurting him. 'Damn! I don't know where we're going.' He paused ominously. 'If I were you, I wouldn't risk it.'

Kate broke away in despair. She knew it had to end but that did not make it any easier.

Kate silently objected to being given 'women's' jobs in the regiment but occasionally she let her feelings show as when Lt Colonel Mark Osbourne informed her that Ministry of Defence rules forbade her from taking part in the live-firing exercise in New Zealand. 'I feel totally useless here,' she moaned. 'All I do is push paper about.'

Cool and capable, she knew, however, that it was her duty to tell Sheena Bowles that husband Vinny had been killed. She described it as 'the worst brief of my army career.'

Kate continued to win friends in high places, among them General Fairhurst, the Colonel of the Regiment, and his ADC, Captain Mike Davidson. She

Despite the odd hiccup, Kate and Kieran cemented their relationship in Cyprus.

took quite a shine to the athletic Davidson until Captain Kieran Voce took her to one side and told her that Davidson was married.

Kieran Voce had an ulterior motive in alerting Kate to Davidson's duplicity. He had grown extremely fond of Kate and, during the later stages of their posting in Germany, romance slowly started to blossom.

Kate remained cautious at first. She told Sandra Radley, the Major's wife: 'After that fiasco with Mike Davidson, I'm scared of letting myself go.'

'Kieran really cares for you,' said Sandra. 'He's a good man, Kate. And they're a bit thin on the ground, as you know.'

Kate and Kieran danced together at the University Ball. They were comfortable in each other's company, her reservations dissolving by the minute. When they went out on to the terrace for some air, he told her that he loved her. After a lingering kiss, he whisked her upstairs to his room, ordered champagne and they slipped between the sheets. Kate had broken her golden rule about mixing business with pleasure. But

'I know you and Kieran are both capable officers and if anything were to happen to you, you wouldn't let personal feelings prejudice good order and military discipline.'
Lt Colonel Nicholas Hammond addressing Kate Butler

this was the real thing and, on the eve of his departure for Bosnia, Kieran proposed. Kate readily accepted.

Her forthcoming status had its drawbacks, however. She became deeply concerned about his posting to Bosnia. 'You don't get it, do you?' she told him. 'I'm a professional soldier – committed, ambitious. Right. But I'm also like all the wives – Joy Wilton, Donna Tucker. You're going into a war zone and that scares me.'

Kate did not go to Bosnia but, when the regiment left, she was made acting captain. She then went to the Junior Division of Staff College on a six-month course for career advancement where she excelled. She then landed a job as assistant to the Director of Public Relations (Army) based at the MOD in Whitehall.

After Bosnia, Kieran, as acting major, took 'B' Company on exercise to Cyprus. There he met up again with an old flame, Flight Lt Louise Everett, based with the RAF at Akrotiri. In Kate's absence, Everett flirted with Kieran. She invited him for a picnic where the last course was a kiss.

'Do you feel guilty now?' she asked him afterwards, savouring the moment.

'Yeah.'

''Cos you're thinking about Kate?'

'No, because for a moment I didn't.'

They kissed again. Kieran could not help himself.

> *'You have to be sure that this will never happen again. If it does, I won't be here for you, Kieran.'*
>
> Kate's warning after Kieran's dalliance with Louise Everett

When Kate arrived in Cyprus on leave, Kieran was eager to put an end to any misconceptions which Louise may have harboured. His future was with Kate, not her. He wanted to forget all about the picnic and the accompanying kisses. As he started behaving coolly towards Louise, she became increasingly annoyed.

'What do you want, Louise?' he demanded.

'Well, not being brushed off like a fly would be a start.'

'I kissed you – that's all.'

Louise was determined to make things difficult for him. 'Do you kiss lots of people?'

'Come on,' bristled Kieran. 'What's your problem?'

Louise was equally irate. 'No, Kieran. What's your problem? I'm not used to being treated like this.'

'Look, if it's your pride I've offended, I'm sorry. If it's your dignity, I apologise. If you need to hear this, I still find you very attractive, Louise, but I don't have the time, the will, the need or the dishonesty right now to have an affair.'

Kate soon sensed that something was amiss and challenged Kieran who told her all about Louise, past and present.

'Louise Everett's an old friend; I haven't seen her since school. We went sightseeing once, that's all.'

'It might have been nicer if I'd heard it from you, not the battalion telegraph,' said Kate.

Kieran stood his ground. 'She kissed me. I kissed her. That was it.'

'Oh Kieran!' sighed Kate in despair. 'Is that all it takes? An old girlfriend shows you her cleavage and that's it? We're supposed to be engaged for Christ's sake. Do I mean so little to you?'

She stormed off to confront Everett.

'I'm about to make a decision that's going to affect the rest of my life,' began Kate, 'and whether I like it or not, you're now a factor. I'd like to know how you see things.'

'"Things" being Kieran?' answered Louise with a touch of arrogance. 'Kieran came out with me of his own free will and he kissed me, nothing more, of his own free will. I'm very fond of him. I'm not going to make any moves but I'm not going to quietly disappear. So it's up to him really, isn't it?'

Her mind still in turmoil, Kate visited Garvey in hospital, where he was slowly recovering from his accident, and sought his advice.

'I'm sure there's nothing in it, ma'am,' he told her, ''cos it's obvious to all of us that he's completely nuts about you. You know, I was faithful to Nancy all through our marriage. What a big success that was!'

'Are you saying it's all right for him to play around?'

'No, no, it's just ... whatever he's done, is it really worth losing everything for? I just think that if you've found the right person, you should do everything you can to hang on to them. I didn't – and I wish I had.'

Kate heeded Garvey's words of wisdom and when Kieran apologised to her, they were reunited.

The wedding preparations were fraught with difficulties, principally caused by the respective parents. Kate's mum, Mary, could have fussed for England and could not appreciate that Kate had everything under control. Meanwhile, Kieran had to cope with his blunt-talking dad Tommy, affectionately known as 'the old reprobate'. Tommy was particularly disapproving of Kieran's choice of best man, Matt Shorrocks, recalling how he had been sick

in the porch at Kieran's twenty-first. Clearly, Tommy had never forgiven him. His concern was not misplaced for, at the stag night, a drunken Kieran ended up centre stage at a strip club. As a result, Tommy refused to allow Shorrocks to take charge of the rings the next day.

The reason for Mary's anxiety became clear. She was sad that Kate would not have anyone to give her away (Kate's father was dead) and the wedding was making Mary miss him all the more. Eventually, Mary regained her composure and lent Kate her locket for the ceremony. Mother and daughter were reconciled. That left just one black cloud on the horizon – the weather. Gales on the night before the wedding had blacked out the hotel at which the reception was being held and had brought down a huge tree in the grounds, thus blocking access for both

Kate and Kieran eventually went through a full military wedding.

caterers and guests. It seemed that the reception might have to be cancelled until Lt Jeremy Forsythe recruited an electrician and press-ganged some of his platoon to shift the fallen tree. The band did not make it, however, leaving the men to form an impromptu group, with Tommy stepping in on keyboards and Tucker taking lead vocals.

No sooner were they married than Kate was offered a three-month PR posting to Belize. She agonised over whether to accept but Kieran, after initial reservations, advised her to go.

'There's still a huge part of me that wanted to say no, Kieran,' she admitted. 'I don't want us to be separated.'

'Belize isn't that far,' replied Kieran, trying to keep his emotions in check. He always was better at diplomacy than geography.

Tom and Laura Cadman

Tom Cadman was marked down for the army at birth. After all, his father was a colonel and in the area of rural, middle-class Surrey where Tom was raised, boys became either army officers or surgeons. Tom was a bit of a cold fish at school: academically bright but not particularly popular. He was often a target for bullying and practical jokes and once spent an entire geography lesson covered from head to toe in flour after one elaborate prank. Thus it was with some relief that he left school at eighteen for Sandhurst where he was able to start with a clean slate.

Ever since her parents bought her a pony for her eighth birthday, Laura Carpenter had always wanted to work with horses. As a leading

Tom Cadman, one of the old school.

light of her Hampshire riding club, she won countless gymkhanas and had ambitions to run her own stables. But when she was seventeen, her lawyer father, to whom she was very close, died of a heart attack. Money became tight, putting an end to the planned stables, and Laura sank into depression. She needed a purpose to life and found it in 1982 when she met and married Tom Cadman. Shortly afterwards, they had a son, Guy, who was eventually dispatched to boarding school. It was the Tom Cadman way.

Tom Cadman, known to all as 'Major Tom', was one of the old school, a traditional army officer who felt that the army had never quite recognised his potential. He even seriously began to consider whether his future lay in the army or on civvy street. He was an honourable man who earned the respect and friendship of his men by usually being scrupulously fair. He could sometimes be a bit of a wet blanket – Dan Fortune once remarked that Tom could stop a party with one judicial remark.

Having been raised on her parents' dinner parties, Laura was a model hostess as well as an accomplished cook. The only problem was she tended to have a little too much cooking sherry and would often have to make a mumbled departure for bed before the party was over. The more insecure she felt, the more she drank. She felt like a second-class citizen, an appendage to her husband whom she considered to be far more intelligent than she was. She tried to talk to Tom about her concerns but he was always too busy playing soldiers to listen. With Tom on duty in Northern Ireland, she sought a solution to her loneliness and despair by embarking on an affair with Major 'Dickie' Bird of 'D' Company.

Laura and Tom have a heart-to-heart.

In Northern Ireland, there was a personality clash between Cadman and Lt Nick Pasco. Hard though he tried, Cadman could not bring himself to like the younger man whose view of the army was vastly different from his own. Pasco used phrases like 'man management' whereas Cadman remained firmly rooted in the days of 'military discipline'. So, on their return to England, Cadman was none too pleased to learn that Laura had invited Pasco and his school-teacher girlfriend, Juliet Grant, round for drinks.

'You've had everything you ever wanted from this marriage. You wanted Guy to go to boarding school – he went. Then you went off to Northern Ireland and left me alone in this soulless bloody house – our ninth, did you know that? Everything you've ever wanted, you've had. Why should I fight for this bloody marriage? Good riddance to bad rubbish!'

Laura Cadman venting her feelings to husband Tom

'What were you thinking about, Laura?' asked Tom, irritated. 'Were you sober?'

Laura did not need snide comments like that. 'No, if you must know, I was paralytic at the time, cooking my socks off for you and knocking it back like a navvy as usual. And now I'm going upstairs to sleep it off – as usual. All right?'

For once, Tom was rendered speechless.

By now, there was a complete breakdown in communication between husband and wife which even Guy's return from boarding school could not repair. Tom was certain something was wrong but could not put his finger on it. However, 'Dickie' Bird's affair with Laura had been going for six months and now, with Tom home and Bird himself about to leave the army, it was make your mind up time for Laura. Should she opt for the excitement of Bird, a renowned womaniser with one failed marriage already behind him, or she should she stay with boring, dependable Tom? It was a tough decision, but Bird wanted a quick answer.

Early one morning on the day before the patrol competition, while Cadman was out playing golf with Guy, Bird called at the house.

'I want to know whether I'll be leaving alone or with you,' he told Laura.

Laura could not give a firm answer. 'It was always in the future – all sort of a dream. I can't ...'

After much agonising, Laura chose to reject 'Dickie' Bird.

SOLDIER

'It doesn't have to be a dream, does it?'

'Look, you're leaving the army and it's a big bad world out there. You want someone to lean on, someone to take away the loneliness. I can't decide now. I'll tell you what I've decided when you come back.'

Cadman spotted Bird leaving the house and immediately put two and two together. He brooded over breakfast.

'What is it, Tom?' asked Laura, breaking the silence.

'I saw Bird leaving. It all makes sense suddenly. While Guy and I ...'

'I'm sorry.'

'When I think of all the poor sods who've come to me about their wives carrying on while they've been away, and I never thought for one minute ...' His pride was hurt. '"Dickie" Bird! "Dickie" bloody Bird! How long? Do you know what you've done to me?'

After taking out his anger on Guy's swingball in the garden, Tom caught up with Bird.

'I could complicate your life tremendously,' he warned his love-rival. 'There'd be no blaze of glory for you: reduced pension, disciplinary hearing, your leaving date delayed, or I could wipe that stupid grin off your face.'

'I don't think that you've given very much thought to this,' sneered Bird.

'Knee-jerk reaction, you think? You're probably right.'

At that, Cadman kneed Bird in the groin. With Bird curled up in pain, Cadman launched a verbal assault. 'What a shallow, useless prick you are!' Bird was too winded to respond. You'd better not mess with 'Major Tom'.

The next task was to humiliate Bird's company in the patrol competition. With Pasco's assistance, Cadman totally outwitted Bird who was captured and dragged back through the river. Cadman was delighted at his company's victory but was not sure what to expect when he went home. He had told Laura that if she was leaving, he would be grateful if she were gone by the time he returned from the competition.

Bird got there first but it was not his lucky day.

Laura told him: 'You've had your fling and I have too. I accept that, but this is where it ends.'

Bird was not a gracious loser. 'Look at us right now. He's back there somewhere with his lads but I'm here. Which do you want – you and me together or him always somewhere else, doing something else?'

Laura would not be swayed. The bitter Bird confronted Cadman in front of Fortune. 'You stitched me. What you can't do in bed, you'll make up for one way or another.' Fortune placed him on leave until his departure from the army. Cadman returned home to find Laura waiting with her suitcase packed. She did not know whether he would still want her but when he asked her to stay, she agreed. Although it would take time to mend their marriage, she assured Tom that she would stand by him, regardless of where his future lay.

Tom Cadman did eventually leave the army and is now a senior executive with a petroleum company. Laura still cooks wonderful business dinners but these days goes a little easier on the sherry.

SOLDIER
SOLDIER

Joe Farrell and
Colette Daly

Keen to see the world and find adventure, Joe Farrell left his native Liverpool with the minimum of qualifications but the maximum in enterprise. Travelling through France, he joined the French Foreign Legion, spending five years in the elite parachute regiment. While based in Corsica at the start of 1994, he met Colette Daly and they returned to the UK. He went through a succession of jobs – some lasting less than a day – but was unable to settle into any of them. He hankered for the excitement of the Legion and decided the next best thing would be to join the British Army. Tucker wasted no time in christening him 'Beau Farrell'.

Twenty-six-year-old Colette Daly is a career woman. Bright and bubbly and extremely ambitious, she used to be a tour guide and now manages a travel agent's. She met fellow Scouser Joe while on holiday

Colette and Joe sometimes seem to be pursuing different goals.

in Corsica but, although she loves him, she is in no hurry to give up her job to become an army wife. Since they are not married, Colette and Joy faced the additional expense of renting their own flat outside the army base. To pay for this, Joe got a part-time job as a cab driver.

Fusilier Joe Farrell joined the King's Own Fusiliers when they returned to the UK from Germany and Cyprus. He and Tucker got off on the wrong foot with Farrell embarrassing Tucker on guard duty at Windsor Castle. Tucker soon realised he had met his match in the cocky newcomer and the pair developed a healthy respect for each other.

Donna envied Colette's independent lifestyle. She told the other wives: 'Colette's not doing what we all did – getting locked into something before we realised what the rest of the world had to offer.' Bemoaning her lot, Donna later voiced her concerns to Colette about doing something with her life. 'Thick as pigshit, me,' said Donna with an honesty that was hard to deny. 'Only thing I left school with was an "O" Level in contraception. I was thinking of doing some classes – adult education.'

Colette's advice was simple. 'Don't think, Donna. Do.'

As events turned out, Colette would have a lot to answer for.

Joe bombarded Colette with marriage proposals but she was happy the way things were. Besides, they had only known each other for eight months. As they drove through town, she could sense another proposal coming on – 'that weird little look in your eye, heavy breathing, sweaty hands. I've seen it all before. I don't wanna marry you, Joe. I wanna be with yer, I wanna share things with yer.'

'You think I'm trying to tie you down?'

'No, I don't; I just don't want to be labelled.'

'How many times do you think a bloke can take getting knocked back? It's not fair me wanting all the time and you just not bothering to give.'

Joe added that just as she was free to go her own way, so was he. Colette did not want to risk losing him and went out and bought herself an engagement ring. It was her idea of commitment. But will it be enough for Joe?

> *'You know what you want to do, son – you want to get her pregnant. Career women, I'd have none of it. I want to get home every night, I want dinner on the table, the TV blaring. I don't want to find a note on the mantelpiece saying: "Sorry, darling, I've pissed off to a convention in Frankfurt."'*
> Tony Wilton offering the benefit of his wisdom to Joe Farrell

Donna, Colette and Isabelle Jennings dress up for the D-Day commemoration.

Jeremy Forsythe

Coming from a large Surrey family with four sisters, banker's son Jeremy Forsythe always saw himself as officer material. Even as a child, he would only join in war games if he could be the general. When it came to the real thing, he certainly had no intention of working his way up through the ranks. Accordingly, at twenty-three he joined the King's Own Fusiliers straight from Sandhurst (where he excelled) and the Platoon Commanders' Battle Course.

When he first joined the King's Own Fusiliers as Platoon Commander, shortly after the platoon returned from Bosnia, Lt Jeremy Forsythe was so wet behind the ears that you could grow rice on his lobes. Fresh-faced and neatly scrubbed, he was every inch the 'new boy', but from the outset he thought he knew it all. This arrogance, combined with a snobbery which led him to underestimate anyone from a different social background, hardly endeared him to the men. Not that Forsythe cared greatly; all he wanted to do was impress the officers. Unfortunately, his immediate superior, Kieran Voce, did come from a working-class background and consequently had little time for the fatuous Forsythe.

'I'd sooner let Sooty run the Armistice Parade!'

Kieran Voce's reaction to Forsythe's offer to help out with the paperwork

As Platoon Commander, Forsythe was hopelessly betrayed by his inexperience of life. Older soldiers, who had fought in Northern Ireland and Bosnia, could hardly go to a young graduate with their problems. And he was no Claire Rayner. When Garvey confided that he had just received divorce papers, Forsythe's less than tactful response was: 'Well, it's not as if it's a big surprise.'

In spite of – or maybe because of – the fact that he was brought up in a house full of girls, Forsythe could be shy and awkward when dealing with the opposite sex. Isabelle Jennings, the CO's wife, tried to bring him out of his shell by installing him as compere for the fashion show in Germany. Not helped by a change of models, he became utterly confused at the microphone. Stanley Unwin would have made more sense.

Forsythe could not resist entering into a bet with another Platoon Commander, Gibson, that he could pass Tucker off as an officer for the night at the Malverns' mess. Sensing the chance of free food and beer at

Forsythe's expense, Tucker accepted, on condition that he could be a captain so that Forsythe would have to call him 'sir'. All went well until Forsythe spotted that Tucker had committed the cardinal sin of wearing white socks and dragged him off to the toilets to black up his socks with boot polish. To pay him back for running up a huge drinks bill, Forsythe later played a trick on Tucker, arranging for him to be 'arrested' by a friendly provost sergeant and driven back to barracks. When Lt Colonel Jennings found out about the prank, he carpeted Forsythe who was obliged to apologise to Tucker and hand over four crates of beer. Tucker 1 Forsythe 0.

'Have you got a brain Tucker? Or is it permanently AWOL?'

The wit of Jeremy Forsythe

Forsythe retained the uncanny ability to rub people up the wrong way. He met a prickly customer in Frank Norton, the FIBUA range warden, who threatened to stop the exercise if anyone upset him.

Forsythe told Stubbs through gritted teeth: 'I've had the lecture on where we can and cannot go and what we must and must not do.'

'Yeah, well, he always was a bit fond of throwing his weight about, sir,' replied Stubbs.

'Evidently,' continued Forsythe. 'But I could well do without him walking into the middle of my exercise and closing us down just because we happen to break a pane of glass or scratch his paintwork. If you ask me, it's bloody ridiculous that a jumped-up caretaker can stop the British Army dead in its tracks.'

But nobody had asked Forsythe, and until he learns to get down off his high horse, nobody will.

Jeremy Forsythe still has a lot to learn.

SOLDIER SOLDIER

Dan and Rachel Fortune

When he was four, little Daniel Fortune almost died after being run over on his way to the ice cream van. He lay in intensive care for a week – doctors told his parents that his chances of survival were less than fifty-fifty. But Daniel was a fighter. Somehow, he pulled through and went on to make a complete recovery. By the age of seven, he was captain of the school football team. He was not gifted academically (he would later remark that his school days were a total disaster) but he did enjoy the sporting side and the character-building which went with it. On leaving school at sixteen, he had a straight choice: either to go into his father's plumbing business or make a career in the armed forces. Forsaking ballcocks and cisterns, he chose the army, joining up as a boy soldier. Over the next thirty years, he worked his way up through the ranks to Lt Colonel. In 1972, he married Sarah but, after nearly fifteen happy years together, she died after a long illness. Ever supportive, Dan nursed her through her last days.

Rachel Elliot loved to write. As a child, she penned poems and plays for her friends and set her heart on becoming a fiction writer. In the end, she settled for journalist. She soon discovered that there was little difference. She began her career on a weekly paper in Watford, covering the usual round of wedding reports, juvenile courts and council meetings. But she had flair (she could even make the annual meeting of the local caged bird society sound interesting) and, at twenty-six, she joined a national newspaper. It was while working there that she met Dan Fortune in a Fleet Street wine bar.

Since he had made it to the top the hard way, Dan Fortune always retained a certain sympathy for the lower ranks. He never forgot what it was like to be a fusilier. As a result, he earned tremendous respect and affection from all of his men,

The family Fortune – Dan and Rachel.

even Tucker, who called him 'the old man'. Fortune was a popular leader: tough when necessary but possessing great charisma.

His charm, energy and availability made him attractive to women but it had taken him a while to get over his wife's death. He had become a little rusty. Rachel set about oiling the wheels.

When the King's Fusiliers embarked on a survival exercise in Wales, Rachel tagged along to write a feature for her paper. Fortune and the Padre, Major Simon Armstrong, flew ahead by helicopter to do an advance recce but disaster struck when the helicopter crash-landed in a forest. Fortune suffered a broken collar bone, the Padre was unharmed but the two pilots were both badly injured. As they built a fire to act as a rescue signal, the Padre and Fortune discussed his relationship with Rachel. At least it helped take their minds of the gravity of their predicament.

> *'I'm like a fish out of water in her world and she is in mine.'*
> Dan Fortune explaining his reluctance to marry Rachel

'When are you going to ask me to marry the two of you?' asked the Padre, cheerfully. 'The Hong Kong posting's a pretty lousy excuse for putting it off.'

'Her job ...', replied Fortune.

The Padre dismissed that as an excuse. 'She can work anywhere. Send her stuff down the phone – by fax, cable, all that.'

'It's been a long time ...', sighed Fortune.

'And it'll be a damn sight longer if you don't pull your finger out. I don't see them lining up at the door.'

Fortune was also concerned about the age difference between them (he was ten years older than her). He broke off from their conversation to check on the injured pilots. One of them had died.

The second pilot was ailing fast. As Fortune and the Padre tried to resuscitate him, a rescue helicopter approached but was unable to land because of the trees. When help finally arrived in the form of Garvey and Butler, they stretchered the stricken pilot to a clearing where the helicopter could pick him up. After a brief reunion with Rachel, who had been beside herself with worry back at the camp, Fortune too was taken to hospital. Bullied again by the Padre, he finally asked Rachel to marry him when she came to visit him in hospital the following evening.

Thus it was as Mrs Fortune that Rachel flew out to Hong Kong, having landed a nice little number as her paper's Far East correspondent. But the honeymoon was quickly over as she began to appreciate the constraints on her husband's time. She had not realised that she would often have to share him with forty other army wives. She did her best to fit in, offering help and advice to troubled wives, while he saw his role in Hong Kong as something of a British ambassador. So when Major Bob Cochrane faced charges of raping his Chinese girlfriend, Yat Sen (her father, Tak Cheng, was an influential member of the community), Fortune was only too aware of the implications.

He rounded on Cochrane: 'One of the last British regiments to serve here and what happens? A scandal that will have half of Hong Kong up in arms. How the hell could you be so stupid? This is bloody

embarrassing. And if it's made official, we're going to have Whitehall screaming down our necks by tomorrow.'

Fortune wanted to protect Cochrane but was warned by Rachel: 'You can't always go out on a limb for your men.'

At Fortune's suggestion, Cochrane reluctantly pleaded guilty to the lesser charge of assault. In return, Tak Cheng agreed to drop the charge of rape. But Fortune was unable to save Cochrane's military career and the Major was given a dishonourable discharge out of the army.

Fortune and the Padre struggle clear of the stricken helicopter. Their attempts to save one of the pilots proved to be in vain.

The night which cost Cochrane his career.

Fortune's next crisis in Hong Kong was closer to home. Working on a feature about illegal immigrants, Rachel went to interview a contact, Mui Ling. Arriving at the flat, Rachel found the woman dead and a two-year-old boy crying. Gripped with compassion and panic in equal amounts, she picked up the child and took him home, resolving to look after him until she could reunite him with his father who was also an illegal immigrant. She phoned the police anonymously to tell them of the mother's death.

When Fortune discovered the child, he was horrified.

'We have to keep the baby until they can be reunited,' pleaded Rachel.

'Are you out of your mind? What if the police find out?'

'They won't. They're illegal immigrants – there's no record of them.'

Fortune was adamant. 'That child has got to go, and it has got to go now. You've got to inform the social services before you get any deeper into this.'

'They'll only put him in an orphanage. He has a father – he needs to be with his father.'

'Have you any idea of the position you've put me in? Harbouring the child of an illegal immigrant. I'm here to keep IIs out!'

'Ok, go ahead. Shop your own wife, you shit!'
Rachel Fortune to husband Dan

'Don't shout,' snapped Rachel. 'You'll wake the baby.'

'You've got to go to the authorities,' persisted Fortune. 'You've got to tell them what's happened. If you don't, I will. I'll have to.'

Rachel couldn't believe what she was hearing. 'You'd really do that?'

'I'll have no choice.'

Rachel responded by moving into a hotel with the child.

Fortune mellowed a little and visited Rachel in the hotel, spending the night with her. Although increasingly attached to the little boy, she eventually handed him over to his father whom she had managed to trace. It was a huge wrench but she knew it was for the best.

The waiting game. Dan anguishes over the regiment's future.

An even bigger wrench was about to face Dan Fortune. Defence cuts meant the regiment would have to be amalgamated. He told Rachel that he had no desire to stay on and oversee the end of the King's Fusiliers. He was going to leave the army.

'It was always my ambition to command the regiment,' he told her. 'I've done that. Now I'm sick of waiting for the axe to fall. It feels like time to get out.'

The Fortunes returned to Britain before the regiment's posting to New Zealand. Rachel has gone freelance while Dan works as head of personnel for a multi-national company. Rachel would still love to start a family but realises that, with each year that passes, time is increasingly against her. In the meantime, she contents herself with two Bernese mountain dogs – and a husband successfully reclaimed from the army.

Ian and Isabelle Jennings

With a brigadier for a father, Ian Jennings' future was mapped out at an early age. He idolised his father and never had the slightest doubt about following in his footsteps. He was attracted to the army by the ideal of being part of a heroic tradition. A natural leader, he was a unanimous choice as school head boy and passed his exams with flying colours. After graduating from Sussex University with an honours degree in modern history, he excelled at Sandhurst where he met his future wife Isabelle at a ball. A keen sailor, chess player and fluent linguist, he did some intelligence work in the Middle East before seizing the chance to join the King's Own Fusiliers as Commanding Officer on their return from Bosnia.

At thirty-seven, Isabelle was three years younger than her husband. Her father and brother were in the army so when she met Ian, there were no surprises. A well-educated woman, she gave up her own career at Sotheby's to be a soldier's wife but continued to collect and sell military prints. Ian used to complain (jokingly) that the house often resembled a picture-framer's workshop. They have two children, Annie (12) and Rachel (11), both of whom were at school in England. Although Isabelle missed them, she firmly believed that a stable existence at school was better for them than the continual upheaval to which army kids are invariably subjected.

Ian and Isabelle Jennings were a popular couple who received many invitations to cocktail parties and suppers. Ian was seldom ruffled and had a quiet natural authority, tempered with a sense of humour and a belief that rules should be interpreted sensibly rather than adhered to rigidly. He was convinced that he was the best soldier in the regiment and made a point of ensuring that he was capable of doing every exercise – he could still crawl for three miles on his stomach even if he was a

Lt Colonel Ian Jennings – a natural air of authority.

shade slower than a new eighteen-year-old recruit. All of his men held him in high esteem, none more so than CSM Michael Stubbs. The two men went back a long way. Stubbs looked after Jennings years ago when the latter was on the way up; now it was Jennings' turn to repay the favour, particularly when Stubbs' irrational behaviour turned out to be the result of post traumatic stress disorder. He reassured Stubbs that the illness and treatment would not affect his career and reminded him that he was not just his CO but also his friend.

Since he set high standards for himself, Lt Colonel Jennings expected the same from others. Sometimes the pressure spilled over on to his family. When daughter Annie visited her parents in Munster during half-term, Isabelle commented on

'You don't want a failure on your hands do you, Dad?'
Annie Jennings

her excellent school report. Then Annie dropped the bombshell that she was not going to take her GCSEs and did not want to go back to school. The reason? She had cheated in a maths exam. Horrified, Isabelle took the problem to Ian.

Annie poured out her heart, blaming the pressure of expectation. 'I'm no good at maths,' she said. 'I've never been any good. They were going to downgrade me unless I got 75 per cent in the test. I had to cheat. I had no option. Everyone wants me to do well. Everyone's always going on about my future, what they think's best for me. No one asks what I want.'

'Of course we want you to do well,' replied Jennings calmly, 'but not if it makes you unhappy.' He suggested that she told the school she had cheated before they found out.

In addition to supervising the regiment's return to England, Jennings was entrusted with the task of organising, with a little help from Isabelle, the D-Day commemorative event. The unplanned highlight was Joy Wilton being rushed to hospital in a Second World War ambulance to give birth to baby Lauren.

What with the kidnapping of Lauren and the death of Wilton, Jennings' last few months in charge of the regiment were highly traumatic. But he dealt with everything in his usual authoritative but compassionate manner. His qualities did not go unnoticed and he was promoted to brigadier. His only regret was that his father was not alive to see it happen.

Isabelle threw herself into preparations for the D-Day commemoration event.

SOLDIER
SOLDIER

Eddie Nelson

Eddie Nelson never knew his father. He and his three brothers and one sister were raised by their mother who faced a constant struggle to make ends meet. Steady Eddie became something of a father figure to his younger brothers and tried to set them a good example. On leaving school, he joined the police force but found his patch in south-east London a complete nightmare – he could not bear being

Eddie Nelson (right) soon became one of the boys.

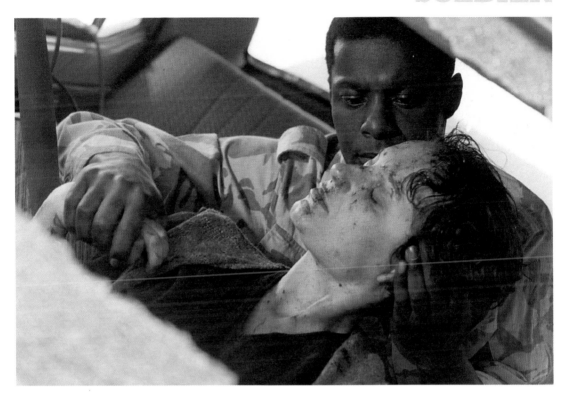

Eddie showed his sensitive side in Cyprus when helping to rescue Athina from a car crash.

disliked by so many people. Seeking something which was more of a physical challenge, he turned to the army, as did his brother, Clive. The wayward Clive could not stand the discipline but Eddie was made of sterner stuff. During training, his aptitude was noticed by the officers who suggested that he join the Signals Corp. He resisted and, at twenty-three, joined the King's Own. Although away from home for months on end, he still felt a responsibility towards his family and regularly sent money to his mother.

As a black soldier, Fusilier Eddie 'Horatio' Nelson was used to racial prejudice. What he was not expecting was to be given a tough time by another black soldier, Colour Sergeant Ryan of the Royal Marines, while on Exercise Lion Sun in Cyprus. Ryan was less than impressed by Eddie's level of fitness (not helped by over-indulging in the local brandy) and warned him that he would not be getting an easy ride just because of the colour of his skin. 'I'm not one of the brothers,' said Ryan ominously.

'Commitment's for life, Eddie. You can't just pick and choose – it's not fair. Anyway, that's the past. I've got you now.'
Eddie's girlfriend, Melanie

Nelson redeemed himself by locating and helping to rescue a woman trapped in her car following a crash. The car was perched precariously on the edge of a cliff and the woman, Athina, needed someone with her to provide reassurance during the rescue attempt. Nelson volunteered and crawled into the vehicle where he quickly established a rapport with her. She was pulled free and Nelson managed to scramble clear just before a rope snapped, sending the car plunging over the cliff. At the hospital, he tried to renew his relationship with Athina but she told him that her father would not approve. Eddie put it down to experience.

When the regiment returned to England, Eddie met Melanie. She was a faster mover than Michael Schumacher. They had barely shaken hands before she had started looking at flats. Eddie tried to cool it but Melanie played her trump card, the unhappy childhood. She had been abandoned by her mother. Eddie was racked with guilt. He knew he was only putting off the inevitable and thought it best to be straight with her before she started knitting baby clothes.

'I know we had a kiss,' he said. 'I just want to be your friend, that's all.'

'I thought you were different. I thought you wanted different things to your mates. When you said all that stuff about your dad walking out and that, I thought we felt the same way. I thought we were after the same things.'

'We are,' answered Eddie, 'only not together.'

Melanie stormed off, bitterly upset.

Shortly afterwards, the Wiltons' baby went missing during the charity five-a-side football match. Eddie feared that Melanie, who had been hanging around, may have taken little Lauren. After all, she was in emotional turmoil and had made it abundantly clear that she longed for a baby. Eddie took his suspicions to Jennings who notified the police. They drove Nelson to Melanie's favourite riverside spot. At first, she was pleased to see him, thinking that he had come to patch things up. Then she spotted the police car in the background.

'You didn't come because you wanted to see me,' said Melanie. 'You came 'cos you thought I'd taken the baby. You really believed it, didn't you?'

Eddie tried to explain. 'You were upset ...'

Melanie was stunned. 'How could I take a baby away from its mum? How do you think I could do that, Eddie? Is that all you think of me?'

She walked off in disgust. It was the last Eddie ever saw of her.

Eddie's younger brother Clive was the black sheep of the family. He had always been trouble. So Eddie was none too pleased when he, Joe Farrell and a new Fusilier, Sticky Collard, bumped into Clive in a pub. Sticky and Clive got on famously, sharing an interest in jazz, and Clive invited him along to his club later in the week. After having to be carried home from the club, Sticky collapsed on an exercise. McCudden suspected that Sticky may have taken drugs and Eddie immediately jumped to the conclusion that Clive must have spiked his drink.

> *'All you ever did was tell me where I was going wrong. You never said anything good about me. You were always perfect. You always did the right thing. Police, army, now social worker.'*
>
> Clive Nelson admonishing brother Eddie

Eddie asked Farrell: 'He was with Clive, wasn't he, before he got into that state?'

Farrell thought better of Clive: 'I know you've got it in for your brother, but I don't believe he'd do that.'

'No, I don't believe that either,' said Eddie firmly. 'I never have. I didn't believe it when the police brought him home that first time for nicking, I didn't believe it the first time the school suspended him for doing drugs!'

Clive denied everything but Sticky was tested positive for drugs and discharged from the army. Eddie remained convinced of his brother's guilt and went to apologise to Sticky.

'Sorry, Sticky, this is partly my fault.'

'How d'you work that out? It was me that got things wrong.'

'No, most of this is down to my brother, but I should have known what he was after.'

'Clive's all right. You can't blame him. All I was trying to do was fit in, be one of the lads. That's all I ever wanted. I was getting more and more screwed up, so I asked Clive for something.'

'You knew you were taking drugs?' said Eddie, incredulously. 'I thought you were straight up. I even convinced myself that Clive spiked your drink.'

Not for the first time, Eddie Nelson had proved a lousy judge of human nature. He was so shaken by the episode that he decided to quit the army. Still trying to find his niche in life, he is currently working as a lifeguard at a swimming pool in north London.

Tim and Sandra Radley

The son of a diplomat, Tim Radley by-passed a generation by choosing a career in the army (his grandfather had been a colonel). After Sandhurst, he saw active service in Northern Ireland. Seeing Fortune leave the King's Fusiliers for civvy street merely confirmed Major Radley's enthusiasm for army life and he helped Lt Colonel Mark Osbourne negotiate the merger of the regiment with the Cumbrians and the Duke of Rutland's Own. In 1980, at the age of twenty-three, he married Sandra and a year later, she gave birth to their daughter, Jessica.

As the daughter of an army officer, Sandra Burnham was used to mixing in military circles. When she met Tim while studying for a degree in economics she had already had her heart broken by one officer. Undeterred, she married Tim soon afterwards. On leaving university, she worked in a City of London bank but gave that up when she had Jessica. With her new daughter to occupy her time, Sandra was suited to army life at first. She enjoyed socialising with other officers and their wives but, as Jessica grew up, Sandra became frustrated and bored. The Radleys' marriage went through a sticky patch. She agreed to stay – but on the understanding that she needed a life of her own.

In Germany, Sandra kept herself busy by working as a part-time teacher. Tim, meanwhile, was a part-time husband and father. No sooner had he returned from an exchange with the Germans than he arranged an exercise which meant spending more time away from home. When Jessica asked him to come along to

> *'Why does daddy always have to be so grumpy? I'm glad he's going away on this exercise.'*
> Jessica Radley

Tim Radley's problems at home sometimes affected his judgement at work – as Garvey discovered to his cost.

her pony classes (she was preparing for an exam), he said it was out of the question. He simply did not have the time but fretted about his daughter having to miss a lesson. This was too much for Sandra who forcibly voiced her feelings.

'Tim, who do you think does everything when you're off on these jaunts? Don't worry yourself. I'll take Jessica to the stables, I'll pick her up, I'll rearrange my timetable, I'll scurry back from school. Don't put yourself out – we'll manage!'

While Tim was away, Sandra received a surprise visit from her old flame, Major Adam Burge. As an army vet, he took great interest in Jessica's pony classes and gave her extra riding lessons. Single and unattached, he was also extremely keen on Jessica's mum. When Tim discovered that Burge was on the scene, he was jealous. He confronted Sandra who denied that anything was going on.

Tim did not believe her. 'You've hardly been apart since he got here.'

'You don't know who I see,' she countered. 'You're never around, are you?'

Tim gave her an ultimatum. 'I want you to tell me you won't see him again.'

Sandra grew tired of Tim's prolonged absences.

She was prepared to give no such assurance but, after Burge made a clumsy attempt to seduce her, she realised that her future lay with her husband. Burge slunk away. Sandra decided it was time to tell Tim a few home truths. 'Yes, I had a relationship with Adam but that was in the past. I've really enjoyed seeing him. He's been attentive and flattering and that's not something I've had from my husband lately. I want this marriage to work. If you give the battalion all your time, you'll have nothing left for us. You've got to meet me half-way on this, Tim.'

'As soon as I saw Sandra, I could tell she's not happy. You can't blame me if your marriage is in trouble.'
Adam Burge to Tim Radley

Tim promised her he would try harder.

Although Radley went to Bosnia with the men (much to Jessica's anguish), Sandra's lecture appears to have had the desired effect. He may still be fully committed to the army but he does now manage to spare some time for his family. And that was all they ever asked.

Michael 'Midnight' Rawlings

Michael Rawlings had a torrid upbringing. He never knew his mother who abandoned him as a baby, leaving him to be brought up in a home. He only saw his father occasionally. Despite such emotional handicaps, he had remarkable confidence and always took the starring role in his junior school play. Alas, he was also rather accident-prone with the result that, during one nativity play, he tripped over the crib, sending the baby Jesus hurtling into the front row and bringing the walls of the inn crashing down on to the Three Wise Men. While the Virgin Mary was treated for mild concussion, Michael received a hearty round of applause. On leaving school, he tried his hand at painting and decorating but this met with equal calamity when he misunderstood his instructions and put up Thomas the Tank Engine wallpaper in the lounge of a High Court judge. Strapped for cash, Michael was drowning his sorrows in the pub one evening when a pal suggested he try the army as a career. The idea held immediate appeal and he went along to the nearest Army Information Office the next morning. Before long, he was a member of the King's Fusiliers.

'Midnight' and his fellow Fusilier, Dave Tucker, quickly became the scourge of the regiment, forever playing jokes on each other. One prank in Hong Kong backfired. During a timed march, instigated by Lt Pereira, Tucker ducked Rawlings in a river. Rawlings complained of feeling ill and later collapsed. The water was contaminated.

> *'Do you know how many men come over here and fall in love with Filipino girls? They meet, it's all romantic and then they come back home and it's a different story. Different culture, different lifestyle. The girls don't fit in and the marriage breaks down. Some of them, all they want is a British passport.'*

Dan Fortune refusing 'Midnight' permission to marry

Rawlings' hopes of romance with Carmita in Hong Kong were doomed to end in heartache.

He continued to wind up Tucker at every opportunity but needed consoling when he received a letter from his fiancée in the UK, saying she was dropping him. 'Midnight' put on a brave face – 'I was going to jack her anyway' – but Garvey, Tucker and Wilton saw it as an excuse to cheer him up at the local 'nightclub', Madam Chow's.

At Madam Chow's, Rawlings met Carmita, a seventeen-year-old hostess, and fell instantly in love with her. She invited him home to meet her grandmother and baby daughter and told him how the rest of her family had been wiped out by soldiers in the Philippines when she was eight, forcing her to flee to Hong Kong. Like him, she was now virtually alone in the world. After just one weekend together, Rawlings returned to barracks and announced that they were getting married.

Everyone attempted to discourage him but Midnight would not listen. Wilton told him he would need permission from Fortune before he could get married. That permission was not granted although the Padre did say that if Rawlings felt the same way about the girl in six months' time, Fortune might reconsider. Rawlings was furious, convinced that he was being victimised because he was black. That evening he brought Carmita to the pub and nearly came to blows with Wilton who referred to her as a whore.

'The army don't own me,' stormed Rawlings. 'I can marry who I like.'

He was in no frame of mind for the junior NCO cadre and walked out of the room mid-way through the written exam. The final phase of the cadre took the form of an initiative test which involved the boys surviving on their wits alone in Hong Kong for twenty-four hours. Rawlings was paired with Tucker.

'Listen, Midnight,' warned Tucker. 'I know you've had a run-in with the army, but you'd better not blow this for me, or I'll have you. Got it?'

'I wanna buy myself out,' said Rawlings.

'You can't buy yourself out. You signed up for three years, you daft git, and you've only done ten months.'

'I'll get myself kicked out then.'

'Look, Midnight, I know how you feel. Getting married! Yeah, well, blokes like you and me, we need that but the way you're going, you won't have anything. Women ... they can let you down, pal. But your mates never will. We're your real family, mate.'

Unimpressed by Tucker's little homily, Rawlings declared his intention to desert. He went off to see Carmita but, at her flat, found her in bed with an American marine.

'I've left,' said Rawlings. 'I've left the army to be with you.'

Carmita was horrified. 'What?'

'It's gonna be fine. We can really be together now.'

'What about money?' hissed Carmita. 'What about a passport? I need a British passport.'

Bitterly hurt, Rawlings realised that Fortune had been right all along. He left the flat in disgust, pausing on the way out to snatch the marine's hat, an item needed to complete the junior NCO cadre. He may have blown his own chances of promotion but at least he had not let Tucker down.

Rawlings was badly injured in the live-firing accident in New Zealand. His shoulder was ripped open and he and Vinny Bowles

Garvey comforted the wounded Rawlings during the tragic live-firing exercise in New Zealand.

were airlifted by helicopter to hospital. On the way, Bowles died. Rawlings was lying next to him at the time.

Bowles' death hit him badly. Vinny was mourned by his loving wife Sheena but Rawlings realised that if he died, there would be nobody to grieve over him. It seemed such a tragic end to a beautiful relationship. How much better it would have been if he had died rather than Vinny. That way, nobody would have been hurt. When Sheena visited Midnight in hospital, he told her that Vinny's dying words had been that he loved her. In fact, such

'If it'd been me, I wouldn't have been able to say I love somebody, 'cos I don't. And there'd have been nobody for anyone to tell about it afterwards. It pisses me off.'

Rawlings telling Kate Butler it should have been him who died, not Vinny Bowles

were Vinny's injuries that he had been unable to speak. But it was a compassionate gesture.

The forthcoming merging of the regiments caused Rawlings to rethink his position. He decided to move on to pastures new. 'It was this amalgamation business that started me thinking, ma'am,' he told Butler. 'If I was made redundant, what would I do in civvy street? So I put in for the Signals – get myself a trade.'

Maybe there was another reason for Rawlings' departure: the presence of Garvey, Tucker and Wilton would have been a constant reminder of the tragic events that afternoon in New Zealand.

Rawlings read a moving address at the funeral of Vinny Bowles.

Michael and Marsha Stubbs

An army child, Yorkshireman Michael Stubbs joined up when he was twenty. The army was his whole life until, ten years later in 1985, he met Marsha, a divorcee with two children, Sarah (7) and Jack (8). Marsha had never met a soldier before in her life but, within six months, they were married. Michael had acquired an instant family. He swore that the iron discipline he received at the hands of his own father would never be repeated on his step-children. While at work Michael was every inch the sergeant major, able to strike fear into the heart of the most hardy soldier; at home he could be tender, loving and caring. At Michael's insistence, although he and Marsha could afford to send them to private school, the children accompanied them wherever he was posted. They went through more schools in more countries than they could remember. The kids took to Michael easily at first, seeing the constant uprooting as a great adventure, but, as they became teenagers, they began to challenge his authority, frequently resorting to the argument, 'You're not my real father'.

Marsha had just got divorced when she met Michael. 'My first husband got the seven-year itch – after five years,' she later remarked.

The Stubbs family in happier times.

She was trying to make it on her own with her two children and had taken on seasonal work at a hotel in Kendal. Michael's regiment, the Cumbrians, were based in Kendal and he used to call in to the hotel for a pint when he was off duty. She did not believe him when he told her that he was a sergeant major. A month after the wedding, they were off on their first posting – to Northern Ireland. Wherever they are stationed, Marsha tries to find work and mix with the natives, as she puts it. She can speak a dozen languages ... or at least order a dozen eggs in a dozen languages.

Even with troubles of his own, Garvey still managed to lend Sarah Stubbs a helping hand.

Marsha threw herself into army life in Germany, taking over the role of organiser-in-chief from Joy Wilton. The difference between Joy and Marsha was that Marsha actually got things done – she did not just talk about it. Fed up with the lack of child care provision, one of the first things she did was establish a crèche. Within no time, it was up and running. Joy would still have been agonising on what colour to paint the walls.

'When it's all over, I shall leave the army and take you two with me. The Sergeant Major will just have to decide where his loyalties lie.'

Marsha laying down the law during the furore over the missing money

The incident where Sarah nearly landed Garvey in serious trouble had made Marsha even more attentive to her children's needs. So with Jack's birthday approaching, she thought about buying him a trail bike.

Michael was not keen. 'I'm not bankrupting meself so as Jack can play at Hell's Angels with a bloody earring through his nose!'

'He's never asked for much, Michael – all the moving around, the upheaval. It's his seventeenth birthday. Before you know it, they're up and gone.'

Michael was unrepentant. 'Yeah, but we can't afford it.' Seeing that the argument was going nowhere, he added bitterly: 'They're your kids – you decide.'

A cheque for £2,000 had just arrived to refurbish the nursery following the fire. The name of an English builder, Clive Hickey, was put forward to carry out the work. He told Marsha, the treasurer, that he could do it for £2,000, but only if it was cash up front. Marsha happily agreed, deposited the cheque in her own account and withdrew the cash to pay Hickey who was coming round that evening for supper with his wife, Steffi, to finalise details. At dinner, it transpired that Hickey had not had a chance to put the quote in writing. Marsha insisted that she could not pay him anything until he had done so.

To Jack's delight, a gleaming trail bike arrived for him, a gift from Marsha. Her pleasure was cut short when Sandra Radley and Joy called round with the suggestion that they go into town to open the nursery bank account. When Marsha went to fetch the money, she discovered to her horror that it was missing. Sandra said she had no alternative but to report the loss. Even Michael was suspicious, particularly since the bike cost £2,000, precisely the sum which had gone missing.

'How did you pay for the bike?' he demanded.

'I paid cash – from my "mad money".'

'What do you mean, "mad money"?'

'It's my insurance against being left again,' answered Marsha, sheepishly. She kept her secret savings in a sewing basket in the bedroom.

Michael and Marsha went to see Lt Colonel Hammond. 'Mrs Stubbs risks being court-martialled,' stated Hammond, 'that is, unless the money is properly accounted for. I'm prepared to regard this as a debt.'

'No, Colonel Hammond,' replied Marsha, 'what you're implying is that I stole the money. I'm sorry, I'm not prepared to consider it a debt and I'm not prepared to pay it back.'

'I must advise you to reconsider,' said Hammond, earnestly. 'We cannot write this money off. The army won't permit it.'

The army's feelings were the least of Marsha's concerns.

Life has rarely been plain sailing for Marsha and Michael.

Kate Butler and Warrant Officer Simms were authorised to investigate the Stubbs' finances. They found the family to be deep in debt, a fact which Marsha had kept hidden from Michael.

He tried to get her to appreciate the seriousness of the situation. 'These people could make life very difficult for us.'

'So you think I should just roll over and pay up, just so I don't screw up your wonderful career?'

'I am not saying that.'

'Well, it's what you're thinking, isn't it? You gonna stand by me, Michael? Are you?'

Receiving no reply, she stormed off for a walk.

Shamed by the kids, who tried to sell Jack's new bike back to the shop owner in order to help their mum, Michael decided to be more supportive. He started making inquiries of his own, centring around the dinner party, and learned that Hickey had been dishonourably discharged from the army. An incriminating envelope, which had contained the missing money, was found in the Hickeys' bin. The culprit, however, was Hickey's wife, Steffi. Marsha was finally in the clear but the wounds would take a while to heal.

The uneasy truce between husband and wife did not last long. Marsha was angry because Michael appeared to be showing little interest in Sarah's education and welfare.

'It was parents' evening, Michael. You're Sarah's dad, even if you're not her father.'

'Are you saying I don't treat her like me own?'

'What I'm saying is, you think you can be a father as and when it suits you, when your work doesn't intervene, when the army wants nothing.'

'That is not fair.'

'The staff didn't have a complimentary word to say about her. Her work's gone downhill. She's become rude and aggressive except in lessons and then she just sits staring at the wall. She's even off her food. It's not like her, Michael.'

'It must be love – or anorexia.'

The first was closer to the mark. Sarah was pregnant by an East German street performer she had befriended. Marsha put pressure on Sarah to have an abortion; Michael urged her to go easy; Sarah said that nobody seemed interested in what she wanted. In despair, she went to stay with Donna who told her she had to make up her own mind. Eventually, she realised she was not ready to have a baby and decided on an abortion.

True to form, Marsha started up a cottage jewellery business in Cyprus. She was offered some gold reproduction jewellery by villa owner Andreas who suggested she take the pieces to Germany as samples to see if she could get any orders. He would pick them up from her later. But when Wilton bought a bracelet to take back to Germany for Joy, he was arrested at Paphos Airport on suspicion of smuggling. The bracelet turned out to be a valuable antique worth over £25,000, stolen from a Cyprus museum a couple of months earlier. Marsha was in hot water until, with the help of Donna and Kate Butler, she managed to 'fit up' Andreas who went on to make a statement absolving Marsha and Wilton of any involvement.

Marsha and Wilton were relieved to be cleared of any involvement in smuggling jewellery out of Cyprus.

When the regiment returned to England, Michael Stubbs began behaving irrationally. Matters came to a head when he made Tucker strip off in the pouring rain and then drilled him around the parade ground in the dead of night. Wilton and McCudden, who witnessed the incident from the guard room, were forced to intervene. Stubbs poured his heart out to McCudden. He admitted that he had been having flash-backs to Bosnia, triggered by hammering sounds which reminded him of a soldier breaking rocks. He described the death of a young soldier who had been stoned to death for no apparent reason.

'They put him up against a wall and stoned him to death. Akim his name was. He was just a lad. I don't know what he'd done wrong – maybe it was 'cos he was talking to me. I always see this soldier and he's breaking rocks. And he's smiling. The bastard is grinning.'

McCudden told Stubbs he was suffering from post traumatic stress disorder, a treatable condition understood by the army. Jennings offered Stubbs his total support.

Meanwhile, Jack had decided to join the army and Sarah had returned to live with Marsha and Michael following the death of her real father, Neil, with whom she had spent the months since her abortion. Marsha was worried that Sarah appeared to be

'He's been behaving very strangely. He's short-tempered, he's moody. You'll be having a conversation with him and one minute he's fine, the next he's off in another world. He's staying out late, he's sleeping with the light on.'

Marsha voicing her fears about Michael's health to Major McCudden

It was the irrational treatment of Tucker which finally brought Stubbs' emotional problems to the surface.

showing no emotion. When the Wiltons' baby went missing a frantic search began. Michael called on Sarah to ask her to give Marsha a hand. He heard a baby cry. It was Sarah who had taken baby Lauren.

Michael knew he had to tread carefully. 'Just tell me, love, why did you take the baby?'

'I don't know. Everyone else is allowed to be happy – you, Joy Wilton. What about me?'

'But we thought you were happy, love. We thought you were coping.'

'I could have had a baby. Only no one was glad for me. Nobody painted me a nursery.'

By now, Marsha had arrived. 'We talked it over, Sarah,' she said softly. 'We did what was best ...'

'What you thought was best,' interrupted Sarah.

'No, love,' said Michael. 'You made the decision. You wanted the abortion.'

'I wanted the baby as well. I'm so sad.'

Marsha hugged her close. 'It's all right. You're not on your own.'

'No,' whispered Sarah, brushing a tear from her cheek. 'Sometimes it just feels like it.'

Lauren was unharmed and McCudden told Marsha that it was unlikely that Sarah would be charged, but she would need treatment.

Jack was being given a hard time at the training depot because of Michael. He went AWOL, driving his parents frantic with worry, before eventually returning home. He vowed never to return.

'I've left,' he said.

'Jack, you're in the army now,' said Michael. 'You can't just leave.'

'Not any more. I've left it.'

'It doesn't work like that.'

'Look, I was no good at it. I hated it, if you really want to know, so I've left. If that's embarrassing for you, well, I'm sorry.'

Jennings was sympathetic. 'Everyone has trouble with their kids.'

'Some of us more than most though, sir,' replied Michael, knowingly.

Michael volunteered to teach Jack self-defence to help him deal with the bullying

> '*It's not so bad for me but for Michael, it's so bloody humiliating. Why are my kids doing this to me? I mean, first Sarah with the baby and now Jack. You just think you've recovered and then, bang, they knock you down again. I must be such a crap mother.*'
>
> Marsha Stubbs on the pains of motherhood

and, if that did not work, he offered to buy him out. 'There's no shame in it,' Michael told him. 'Some battles just aren't worth fighting. Life's too short. I want you to know that whatever happens, I'm behind you.'

That meant a lot to Jack. He had already made up his mind: he was going back to the training depot. He was a battler like his stepfather. And that was not the only good news for Michael. Promotion was on the cards. After all he and Marsha had been through, it was well deserved.

Luke and Bernie Roberts

Although one of the brightest in his class at school, Luke found most of his teachers uninspiring and ending up dropping out of school after his GCSEs. His decision to join the army was partly sparked off by a feeling that here was a chance to work in the real world. He was further encouraged by the recruiting officer who hinted that the army was one place where hard work and initiative could pay off in career terms. He was also motivated to get a steady job because his girlfriend, Bernie, was pregnant and he wanted to do the right thing. She was the only girl he had ever slept with. They got married but, soon after the wedding, Bernie miscarried. Luke joined the Cumbrians and survived the merger because, beneath his cocky exterior, he was a first-class soldier.

Bernie became pregnant while she was at technical college in Cardiff doing a course in computer studies. Since she was a Catholic, there was no question of her not having the baby. She gave up her course – something she subsequently regretted – only to miscarry. She was devastated, but the experience brought her and Luke closer together as a couple and made them even more determined to start a family.

At twenty, Fusilier Luke Roberts was fiercely ambitious. He did not suffer fools gladly; this brought him into immediate conflict with Dave Tucker. When Tucker and Garvey painted out the 'Own' on the 'King's Own Fusiliers' sign in response to their regimental goat being painted blue, Roberts was blamed for it and confined to barracks for a month. Knowing that Tucker was the real culprit, Bernie pleaded with Donna who persuaded Dave and Paddy to confess to their artwork.

> *'Luke reckons his whole career's ruined – it's a mark against him. He wants to get on. He doesn't just want to stay in the army, he wants to do well. The army's his whole life.'*
>
> Bernie Roberts to Donna Tucker

Two years after her miscarriage, Bernie found that she was pregnant again. She and Luke were overjoyed.

'I can just make out an arm,' he said, eyeing the scan. 'It's got three stars on it. He's gonna be a captain!'

*Bernie Roberts had more
than her fair share of
troubles in Germany.*

'He might be a she.'

'Even better – woman captain at the age of nought. Brilliant. Tell
you what, if you're a couple of weeks late, she might be a major!'

Bernie made Luke promise to keep her pregnancy a secret. 'I don't
want everyone fussing over me. All that mother and baby talk, I can't
stand it.'

Also at the back of her mind was the fear that she might miscarry
again. Sadly, her worst fears came true. While Luke was being his usual

resourceful self avoiding capture on an exercise, Bernie was rushed to hospital with complications.

She was sent back home and told to rest, but miscarried. 'You promised me it would be all right,' she told Luke tearfully when he finally surfaced.

Life had to go on. But just as Bernie was getting things back to normal, she was dealt another cruel blow. She was driving towards the Munster barracks when a speeding car, overtaking an army Landrover, forced her off the road on to the cycle track where she

'There wasn't any room. There was a car and a Landrover. I had to swerve.' Bernie reliving her road accident to Sandra Radley

hit a twenty one-year-old student, Gerd. The unconscious Gerd was taken off to hospital and Bernie was quizzed by the German police and the RMP. The German police announced their intention to prosecute, having found a witness who saw Bernie hit the cyclist, but no army Landrover or speeding car.

Bernie could not sleep at night. 'If that boy dies, I'll have killed him, won't I?' she sobbed to Luke.

'It won't come to that. The army'll sort it.' Luke's faith was touching.

Bernie went to visit Gerd in hospital. His mother, Maria, was conducting a bedside vigil.

'It wasn't my fault,' pleaded Bernie.

'Was it his fault?' countered the mother, curtly. 'You were driving the car which hit him. Do you have children, Mrs Roberts?'

'No.'

'Perhaps if you had, you would drive with more care.'

Bernie felt worse than ever.

Then Bernie was granted a slice of overdue luck. As the lads were taking rubbish from the mess cellars to the dump, they spotted Fusilier Martin Smith heading off in a Landrover. Further inquiries revealed that Smithy was notorious for illegally using his Landrover to sneak off and visit girls. Under pressure from Garvey, Tucker and Roberts, Smithy owned up. The prosecution was dropped and Gerd made a full recovery.

The news that young Sarah Stubbs was pregnant acted as another body blow for Bernie. 'It's not fair,' she said. 'Sarah didn't even want a baby, but I did.' It brought back all the sadness of her miscarriages. She told Marsha Stubbs: 'You don't trust anything any more – not even your own body.'

On top of that, Bernie learned that Luke might be going to Bosnia.

He tried to reassure her. 'I love you – I'm not going anywhere.'

'You should know you can't make promises like that. I've lost two babies and now I might lose you.'

When rumour became fact, Luke put a brave face on it but, at the moment of departure for Bosnia, he finally admitted to Bernie that he was scared about going. It was an emotional farewell.

Still happily married, the Roberts were rewarded with the birth of baby Natasha in 1994. At last, they are a complete family.

Kieran Voce

Unlike the vast majority of his fellow officers, Kieran Voce did not come from a privileged, Home Counties background. Comprehensive school educated, he was a working-class lad whose speech, when he got angry, revealed his northern roots. Neither did he come from officer stock: his father was an RSM. As a boy, Kieran remembered being in love with his form mistress when he was five and collecting tadpoles in jars. He worked hard at school and, to celebrate their 'A' Level results, planned to see *Return of the Jedi* with Louise Everett at Wigan Odeon in 1983. He stood her up – it was a decision which would come back to haunt him.

'If I'd stood my ground, we'd never have messed it up.'
Kieran Voce partly blaming himself for the death of Fusilier Vinny Bowles.

While Lt Colonel Fortune and Major Radley were in London negotiating the merger of the regiments, Captain Voce was the acting Officer in Charge in New Zealand. The death of Vinny Bowles made it a harrowing baptism. Although Captain Mercher, the safety supervisor for the live-firing exercise, was to blame, dismissing Voce's reservations and insisting that the men press ahead regardless of a suspected unexploded mortar, Voce could not help feeling partly guilty. He had been aware of the dangers but had allowed Mercher to overrule him. As a result, a young soldier was dead.

In the wake of the tragedy, Kieran Voce quickly endeared himself to the men with his willingness to muck in, although some of his fellow officers tended to look down on him because he lacked a public school education. Radley, in particular, thought he was too friendly with the lads – it was conduct not becoming an officer. When

Kieran Voce discusses tactics with Ian Jennings in Cyprus.

Kieran felt he had not done enough to help Luke Roberts following Bernie's road accident, even Kate Butler, his future bride, felt compelled to offer a piece of friendly advice.

'There is such a thing as getting too involved,' she told him.

'Isn't the men's welfare part of our job?' queried Kieran.

'Of course it is, but only when we can do something about it.'

Kate Butler proved to be the best thing that had ever happened to Kieran. His career has gone from strength to strength and he is now a major. It can only be a matter of time before they erect a statue of him in Wigan.

ABOVE: *Old-flame Louise Everett almost caused serious problems for Kieran.*

OPPOSITE: *Kieran Voce – a man with a bright past and an even brighter future.*

DUNCAN BELL
as LT COLONEL PAUL PHILLIPS

For Duncan Bell, playing an army officer has proved quite an eye-opener. Although he has appeared in countless popular series, including *Taggart, Boon, Medics, Between the Lines, Doctor Finlay, Minder* and *A Touch of Frost*, this is Duncan's first military role.

'In fact, I've never really played people in authority before,' he says. 'I think part of the thinking behind the casting for Phillips was to choose someone unlikely. I certainly fitted the bill!

'Not only is there no military background in my family but they are actually quite anti-army. My father did his National Service and proved to be so good that they asked him to stay on to do officers' training. But he declined. You'll find that a dislike of the army is quite common in the West of Scotland where I come from.'

With no experience on which to draw, Duncan spent a couple of days at Warminster with officers of the Prince of Wales Yorkshire Regiment. 'I arrived with the usual preconceptions but they were quickly blown away. There was none of the snobbery that I'd been led to expect. Different social classes existed quite happily side-by-side, especially among the younger officers. I was surprised at how many different dialects there were among the officers and that gave me the confidence to play Phillips in a Scottish accent. I no longer felt that he would have had to adopt a Home Counties accent to get where he has.

'I was also amazed at how relaxed the officers were. I thought they'd be sticklers for detail – obsessed with highly polished boots and so on – but there was no need for a dictatorial attitude. The feeling was very much that the officers and the men were all in it together and would fight for each other. I found that the worst crime was a lack of enthusiasm, a lack of commitment.'

Paul Phillips could never be accused of lacking enthusiasm. Aged thirty-eight and single, he is a university graduate from a middle-class background who has served with the SAS and won the Military Cross for his bravery during the Gulf War. Now he has been rewarded with the command of a battalion.

'He is very ambitious,' says Duncan, 'and something of a high flier. He loves the army and has made it his life, perhaps to the extent of neglecting his private life. He enjoys a good rapport with the men and doesn't feel the need to act the disciplinarian. He knows that everyone can do their job and will respect his authority. All he has to do is let them know that he's watching them.'

Born in Dumbarton, Duncan did not consider an acting career until studying English at Glasgow University. 'I didn't do school plays – the productions tended to be Gilbert and Sullivan operas – and it wasn't until I became interested in Pinter and Shakespeare at university that I thought about acting. My apprenticeship was two years' touring with the Cheek by Jowl theatre company. I remember a production of *Vanity Fair* in which I had to play a number of different roles. As George Osborne, I died just before the interval, returning as the aristocratic Marquis of Steyne. At that point, I heard a whisper from the audience: "I thought he'd just died?" So much for convincing versatility!'

There was one aspect of army life on which Duncan was not so keen. 'When I was at Warminster, all the officers were getting excited about doing twelve-mile battle fitness training exercises. I managed to steer clear of that – it was well beyond my physical capabilities. So although Phillips is something of an action man, I shall look forward to him spending plenty of time behind his desk ...'

Duncan Bell as Lt Colonel Paul Philips

HOLLY AIRD
as SERGEANT NANCY GARVEY

It was a phone call from former screen-husband Jerome Flynn which led to Holly Aird's return to the ranks of *Soldier, Soldier.*

'Jerome said to me he'd got a great idea for a storyline if Nancy came back. I'd thought about the possibility of returning at the start of the previous series but had never done anything about it. But now seemed the right time. I knew the storylines would be strong – whether or not Nancy and Paddy got back together – and also, with a few people leaving the series, it's good to have an old face coming back.'

At twenty-six, Holly is anything but an old face even though she made her television debut at the tender age of nine in *The History of Mr Polly.* Two years later, she went to Kenya to star in *The Flame Trees of Thika* with Hayley Mills. Holly now serves as living proof that child actors can make a successful transition into adult roles.

'I had all the usual warnings that I'd run out of jobs the moment I started getting spots and boyfriends, but in fact I never really stopped working. I even did an Agatha Christie story for the BBC with my teeth in braces.

'I really enjoyed my first stint on *Soldier, Soldier*', says Holly, herself an army daughter (her dad was in the Royal Scots Guards and Holly was born in the Army Hospital at Aldershot). 'But after two and a bit years, I wanted to move on. I felt I'd done everything I could with the character. I was also worried about being type-cast and, since I had no responsibilities, I could do pretty much what I wanted. But in the past year, I've had five jobs so I thought it was safe to come back.'

Those roles included *Circle of Deceit* with Dennis Waterman, an episode of *Kavanagh, QC, Peaches* at the Royal Court Theatre and the pilot episode of *Rules of Engagement.*

'I was the only girl in *Rules of Engagement.* I played an undercover policewoman – rather like a nineties' version of Purdey from *The New Avengers.* The only thing I didn't like were the guns!'

How does Holly see the future for Nancy and Paddy? 'They've been apart for two years but Nancy never really wanted to leave him. The break-up was all a bit strange – just because she went away on a course for ten weeks. Neither of them tried very hard to keep things together. In spite of that, she's never stopped loving him.

'Now she's passed her sergeant's course, she needs Paddy to be stronger than he was. Obviously, with maturity, she isn't as mad as she was at the start. She's much more sensible although, having said that, I don't want to abandon the fun element in Nancy. When they were married, she was actually growing up faster than Paddy, but now he's caught her up.'

The one thing Holly missed out on in the new series was a foreign posting. 'I never got farther than Windsor this year! But I can't complain because I've had some good trips to Hong Kong and New Zealand. Rosie Rowell went out with the boys to Australia and I thought about going too but I'm glad I didn't because everyone said how hot it was. Anyway, with the money I saved, I bought a house instead!'

If things work out with Paddy, Holly is looking forward to getting a more sympathetic reaction from the public. 'Some people do tend to confuse fiction with reality,' she laughs. 'Shortly after the episode in which Nancy left Paddy, I was walking down the street where I live when a woman grabbed me by the arm and called me a "lousy bitch" for ditching a decent bloke like that!'

Holly Aird as Sergeant Nancy Garvey

ANGELA CLARKE
as COLETTE DALY

Most aspiring actresses quit waitressing for television but with Angela Clarke, younger sister of Margi, it was the other way round.

Angela had moved to London from her native Liverpool and was working as a waitress in L'Escargot, a fashionable Soho restaurant. 'Then one day I saw an advert in the *New Musical Express* for presenter for a new late-night rock show. I got the job, packed in waitressing and ended up as one of the presenters on this show called *Night Network*. I was on a three-month contract but I only stuck it for six weeks. I just hated presenting. The only good thing about the show was working with Nicholas Parsons. So in the end, I ran back to L'Escargot, begging for my waitressing job back!

'I was there for about six months in all. It was really handy because it's in the heart of theatreland and I used to wait on the tables of influential people. I waited on the table of the casting director for a production of *Child's Play* at Hampstead and then the casting director at the National Theatre saw me in that and it led to other parts including a nine-month tour with the Hull Truck Theatre in *Viva Espana*. Looking back, it's no wonder I used to get in trouble because I was always chatting to the customers.'

Now twenty-six, Angela made her TV debut at fifteen. 'I was Damon Grant's girlfriend, Elsa, in four episodes of *Brookside*. At the time I had a crush on Simon O'Brien (who played Damon) and I kept telling the director that Elsa should kiss Damon! When I was sixteen, I appeared in the film, *Letter to Brezhnev*, which was written by my brother, Frank Clarke. Of course, Margi was in that too and we also appeared together in the film *Blonde Fist*. It's great having

her in the business. She's always there if I need any advice and she has a cool head on her.'

Angela's career has been peppered with interesting parts. 'In *Pie in the Sky*, I played someone who was force-fed mushroom soup and I did a French film where I traipsed through fields wearing a chainmail metal bikini in the depths of winter. That was weird.'

For playing Colette Daly, Angela was able to draw on family experience. 'Colette's very independent, a bit vain and a real social climber. She loves Joe but she's still not sure about marrying him. She wants to keep her own identity and that can be a problem for army wives. One of my sisters was married to a soldier and it put a real strain on their marriage. Army wives are just an appendage – the husband's career always comes first. The wives are told how to dress and how to behave. It can make life really difficult. I could never be married to someone in the army.'

One person Angela did hit it off with was David Groves who plays her screen partner, Joe Farrell. 'I clicked with David straight away. He's dead funny – he really cracks me up.'

The effect was not always intentional, however. Angela recalls: 'There was a scene where I was supposed to be driving the car but, because I haven't got a licence, we had to be towed by a van. The scene began with David getting dressed in the car and as I turned to him, I suddenly saw his collar bone sticking out. It's the legacy of an old accident but it gave me the shock of my life. I threw up my hands in horror when I saw this bone but of course the car kept on going. People who were watching and didn't realise we were being towed must have thought the car was like Herbie!'

Angela Clarke as Colette Daly

RICHARD DILLANE
as SERGEANT BRAD CONNOR

After living in Australia for nine years, combining acting and directing, Richard Dillane decided to return to England in July 1994 to try his luck. Six months later, he landed the part of Brad Connor in *Soldier, Soldier* and learned that for his first filming, he would be heading straight back to Australia.

'It was certainly fortuitous,' says thirty-one-year-old Richard. 'After all, it was my first TV work, either in Britain or Australia. I was able to act as guide, showing the other lads the sights, the surf and the pleasures of Australian wine. The British guys were all terrified of red-backed spiders. They thought every time you sat on the loo, you'd get bitten. But it just doesn't happen. And I think they expected to see kangaroos in the high street ...

'During the six weeks we were out there, I also managed to visit my brother Nick, who's a doctor up at Coolangatta on the Gold Coast, and my sister Sarah, who lives at Katoomba.'

Raised in Kent, Richard went out to Australia at the age of twenty-two after graduating from Manchester University. 'My dad's Australian so I grew up with the idea of a second homeland. It made me determined to go, to see what the place was like. I spent five of my years there in Sydney and did a lot of work in theatre and radio. Now I'm back in England but I really don't know where I call home.'

Brad Connor's family moved to Australia before he was born. Chauvinistic and nationalistic, he joined the army to travel the world and escape from his job as a garage attendant. He is a highly skilled soldier who excels in jungle warfare and has trained in many countries including Malaysia, Papua New Guinea, Hawaii and New Zealand. A hard task master, he is not easily accepted by the men although he does respect talent. He has no shortage of female admirers – until they get to know him.

'One of the good things about *Soldier, Soldier*', says Richard, 'is that I've been able to use my Australian background. And the producers are open to input from the actors regarding their characters. They want to avoid stereotypes and it has to be said there is a level of ignorance in the British perception of Australians. So part of my mandate is to flesh out the character, make it authentic.'

Like Brad Connor, Richard has led an eventful life. He has backpacked through Europe, South-East Asia and Australia, was a white-water rafting guide in Tasmania and has worked as a warehouseman, computer clerk, labourer, fruit picker, market research interviewer and wine salesman.

'I've certainly had a few hairy moments. Rafting on the Franklin River in Tasmania was pretty wild – I turned over a few times – but probably the closest shave was when I nearly sat on a deadly tiger snake, also in Tasmania. Luckily, it was really cold and the snake was dormant so it was too slow to bite me. But I wasn't taking any chances – I just ran for my life!'

Richard Dillane as Sergeant Brad Connor

SHAUN DINGWALL
as LANCE CORPORAL STEVE EVANS

Shaun Dingwall's first experience of body-surfing on Australia's famous Bondi Beach nearly left him hospitalised.

'Going out on *Soldier, Soldier* was my first trip to Australia,' says Shaun, 'and, like the rest of the guys, I couldn't wait to get to Bondi Beach. I body-surfed there for about three hours but you have to be really careful because some of the waves are huge. The waves take you along at such speed that you just have to shut your eyes. The first time I did it, I was being carried along when I felt my left hand reach out and grab someone's buttock. It was an instinctive thing – my eyes were tight shut – but I was going so fast that I knew I daren't let go or I'd have fallen off. When we got back to the beach, I saw this guy who was about 6' 6" tall, built like a house, looking around to see whose hand had grabbed him. I just slunk away quietly with my towel between my legs!

'We also had to be careful not to get a sun tan. The three Australian episodes were shot in reverse order – six, five, four – so we had to stay pale to avoid wrecking continuity. In that heat, it wasn't easy.

'The coastline was incredible. We started off at Sydney and then moved north to the coal-mining town of Newcastle. Robson Green felt at home there! We also spent two days in Alice Springs and I found time to visit the amazing Ayers Rock. It was a fabulous experience.'

Filming assignments in Australia are a far cry from Shaun's first tentative steps in acting. 'As a boy, I'd always been interested in computers and physics rather than the arts. Then, at the age of sixteen, I was sitting at home, bored, one Sunday afternoon when I picked up a copy of *What's On In London* and saw an advert for an acting workshop, at the Tom Allen Centre at Stratford East. I went along and there was only one other guy there but I really enjoyed it. I thought, this is the life for me.'

Since then, Shaun's appearances have included a bent cop in *Between the Lines*, an insurance salesman in *Minder* plus roles in *Class Act, The Bill* and the 'Screen Two' production *Genghis Cohn*.

Steve Evans is twenty-three and was brought up in the East End of London. He feels lucky to have escaped from his family since his father and his three brothers spend most of their time down the pub putting the world to rights, drinking away their unemployment benefit. His sister is saddled with two kids and no husband while his mother is past caring. Steve joined the army when he was made redundant during the collapse of the construction industry. He is always strapped for cash, earning him the nickname 'Flush'.

'The army was a way out for him,' says Shaun, 'but he enjoys the life, particularly the boxing. The army is the only thing in his life that he's made a success of and he's determined not to blow it in any way.'

Although there is no military background in Shaun's own family – 'the nearest was that my grandfather was a cook in the Navy' – this is not the first time he has played a soldier.

'I played a lance corporal in the BBC film *A Breed of Heroes*. He was an army photographer. Unfortunately, filming on that only took me to Salford. And by no stretch of the imagination can Salford be compared to Bondi Beach.'

Shaun Dingwall as Lance Corporal Steve Evans

ROSIE ROWELL
as DONNA TUCKER

Rosie Rowell confesses that she is largely to blame for the break-up of the Tuckers' marriage. The thirty-year-old Geordie actress says: 'I felt the character was in danger of getting stale. It was time for her to do something different. Donna was never cut out to be an army wife and she got fed up with Dave chasing other women. When she heard about Dave's paternity suit, it hit her very hard and she realised how sick she was of always playing second fiddle to the army. Then her younger sister, Kelly, turned up in Cyprus and told her a few home truths about traipsing round the world after a no-hoper like Dave.

'Something had to give. I think Donna always reckoned she was a bit brighter than Dave – admittedly, that's not too difficult – so we came up with the idea of educating Donna. And that led to the affair with Mark.

'The thing about Mark was he took her seriously and treated her as an intelligent person. All Dave ever seemed to do was joke and lark around. Donna was tired of the whole "lad" business. She wanted something more.'

Rosie insists that she has little in common with Donna, particularly when it comes to dress sense. 'Donna's a bit of a tart whereas I'm a tomboy. I've been playing her for four years now and each time I find I need more and more persuading to get into Donna's gear. The wardrobe guys will stick me in a micro-skirt and say: "That looks lovely." And I'll slap my lardy bottom and say: "Oh no it doesn't!"

'Personally, I can't stand stiletto heels and tight skirts – I much prefer to wear something loose. But I do find that when I put on Donna's clothes, it really helps me get into the character.

'Over the years, I've come to think of her as my wayward younger sister and you do have to admire her spirit. And I suppose she could be considered quite glamorous – if only by the sort of blokes who fancy Bet Gilroy!

'Funnily enough, when we were out in Cyprus with Tracy Whitwell playing Kelly, onlookers used to think Tracy really was my sister. The similarity between us was uncanny.'

Despite the many differences between herself and her screen alter ego, Rosie's initial experience of London life could have come straight from Donna's CV.

'When I first moved to London from Newcastle, I had to wait three years before being accepted by drama school. I did various jobs, including working as a barmaid in a hostess club where the girls sat around topless. It gave me the creeps because even though I wasn't topless, I still got propositioned constantly. In that kind of place, men assume you're there for their sexual service. I bet the men never went home to their wives and said: "I had lunch today with a girl whose breasts were hanging out!"'

Donna could not have phrased it better.

Rosie Rowell as Donna Tucker

DAVID GROVES
as FUSILIER JOE FARRELL

Wallasey-born David Groves discovered that history was repeating itself when he started playing Joe Farrell in *Soldier, Soldier*. 'My dad is Mick Groves of the folk group The Spinners. They've been going thirty-three years, although they're now semi-retired, and used to have their own TV series, the lot. It meant that people were always coming up to my dad in the street to say hello. Anyway, just before Christmas, I was walking down a street in Liverpool with my brother and somebody recognised me from *Soldier, Soldier*. My brother went spare. He said: "We've just got rid of Dad being recognised and now it's happening again with you!"'

With such a showbusiness background, it was hardly surprising that David should follow a similar career. 'Dad was away a lot on tours – although I used to go with him sometimes – but obviously it introduced me to that world. There was a price to pay though: I used to get the mickey taken out of me at school because of who my dad was. In fact, I hated school. I hated the teachers' attitudes – I didn't respond to some of their Nazi tactics. The only one who treated me with respect was the drama teacher. She taught you, the person, not just the subject.

'When I was sixteen, I was supposed to be going on a debauched camping holiday to Spain with ten mates but the opportunity to join Manchester Youth Theatre came up at the same time. So, although I'd already paid the deposit, I cancelled the holiday and chose the theatre instead. I didn't know what to expect – I thought it might be all poncey actors – but I was glad I went because I had a ball.'

At eighteen, David joined a circus school in Bristol where he learned acrobatics, juggling and tap dancing. He also had a three-month stint at Butlin's, Pwllheli. 'I mainly worked with the backstage crew, doing lighting and sound, but I also did some ballroom dancing. I had to dance with the old folks! I was only paid £53 a week for a fourteen-hour day but I really enjoyed my time there. They were salt-of-the-earth people. The

only person I didn't get on with was the entertainments manager. We had a blazing row and he sacked me, a month before my contract was up.'

From 1989 to 1992, David studied at the Webber Douglas Academy of Dramatic Art. 'Since leaving drama school, I've been really lucky. I had a small part in *The Bill* and then seven months in a play, *Six Degrees of Separation*, at the Royal Court and the Comedy Theatre. It's nice to get the security of a long run early in your career. Then came *Soldier, Soldier*.

'I had certainly never considered the army as a career. Before *Soldier, Soldier*, I would have been a conscientious objector but the programme has changed my attitude towards soldiers. Now I think they're OK, just the same as me. I fell into acting, the same way they fell into the army. I heard I'd got the part of Joe Farrell on the Friday and began filming on the Monday. So I had to pick up the drill straight away. Fortunately, I found it was rather like doing a dance routine. The real squaddies said I did OK, that it had taken them six months to learn that. The worst thing was having to have my hair cut short. I hated it – I looked like something out of Showaddywaddy.

'Joe is a jack-the-lad character,' says twenty-eight-year-old David. 'As a soldier, he's full of beans although he doesn't suffer fools gladly. That's why he gets wound up by Tucker. He likes being controlled by Colette but not by anyone else. Colette is definitely the strong one in the relationship.

'I've already had plenty of laughs on *Soldier, Soldier*. I remember the last day of the previous series was the birthday of Dave Attwood, our military advisor. There was a chocolate cake for him and we thought we'd carry it in for him on Tony Wilton's coffin. The problem was Jerome Flynn. He was at the front but he's so tall that he created an imbalance. The result was the birthday cake fell off and got squashed into a gooey mess. I don't think Dave fancied any after that ...'

David Groves as Fusilier Joe Farrell

JEROME FLYNN
as CORPORAL PADDY GARVEY

Jerome Flynn is delighted that Nancy comes back into Paddy's life for the fifth series.

'A lot of people were saddened by the fact that Nancy left Paddy,' says Jerome, 'and I felt that since the split he had really missed her. In his eyes, none of the women he had met subsequently had matched up to Nancy. He had never wanted to split up in the first place but there were a lot of misunderstandings between them.

'Anyway, Holly Aird and I have stayed in contact since she left. We had enjoyed working with each other and, as this was going to be my last series of Soldier, Soldier, I thought it would be really nice to get Holly back in, to round off the story. It would be a good way of putting an end to Paddy's pain.

'The chance encounter with Nancy comes as a big shock to Paddy, who had become resigned to the fact that he would have to spend the rest of his life without her. But he's very open with his feelings and, although the intention might be to take things slowly, they're in bed together by the end of episode two!'

Jerome enjoyed another reunion while filming the fourth series, for his brother, Daniel, came in to play Paddy's brother Danny, the first time they had acted together since appearing in a youth drama group. It was Jerome who suggested to the producers that Paddy should have a brother, an outside influence who would make him consider his future.

'When they took up the idea, they didn't know I had a brother in real life who acted too. So I suggested Daniel. Everyone agreed he was the obvious choice because we look pretty much alike. The only problem was stopping ourselves from laughing all the time.'

A more serious matter was portraying Paddy's temporary blindness. 'I felt a great responsibility playing a blind person,' says Jerome. 'Since I could still see all the other actors and crew, I was aware that it could easily look totally unconvincing. At the same time, Paddy wasn't used to being blind so I wanted it

to look awkward too. In the end, I just tried not to focus on anything, but it wasn't easy.'

Jerome feels extremely lucky in the amount of travel that Soldier, Soldier has given him over the last five years. 'I always wanted to travel with my work. I love to experience different cultures.' The trip to Australia proved to be quite a learning experience for him.

'The Aborigines are one of the oldest peoples on earth. They are evolved in ways far beyond our understanding. Their culture is inherently non-violent and non-territorial; they believe they are part of the land rather than rulers over it. Along with the other indigenous tribes of the world, they have much to teach us, and I feel we must listen to them if we are to get out of the mess we're in.'

The environment is a subject dear to Jerome's heart and he would like to devote more of his energies towards it in the future. 'When Soldier, Soldier ends, if the right sort of acting job comes up – something that will present an interesting challenge – I'll take it, but I'm leaving my options open. There are a couple of other directions I'd like to explore. There are two drama projects which I would like to get off the ground as a co-writer, but I'm also interested in getting into documentaries about environment issues.'

In the meantime, he is tasting new-found success as a pop star following the release on VE Day of the double 'A' side single, 'Unchained Melody' and 'White Cliffs of Dover', with Robson Green which shot to the top of the charts.

'And we've just finished doing an album,' adds Jerome. 'I've always loved singing – I sang to get my Equity card – but I've never had a good enough voice to be able to hold down a musical. This is all very exciting, but you have to take it with a pinch of salt. I wouldn't want to start taking myself seriously as a pop star! The good thing about doing it with Robson is that he and I look after each other and make sure we keep our feet on the ground. I don't think either of us would have done it if we'd been on our own.'

Jerome Flynn as Corporal Paddy Garvey

BEN NEALON
as LT JEREMY FORSYTHE

Ben Nealon has finally fulfilled his family's ambitions for him – not by becoming an actor, but by joining the army.

'My grandfather was a major in the Desert Rats,' says twenty-eight-year-old Ben, 'and my father was a commander in the Royal Navy until he retired three years ago. They always wanted me to go to Sandhurst to get a commission. It was all mapped out for me. I went to public school at Exeter and while there, I joined the cadets. But when I was seventeen, I rebelled against the cadets. I was fed up with being ordered about by this bawling sergeant major so I told him to shut up and walked out. That was the end of my army career!

'By then I'd decided that I wanted to be an actor, and within six months of leaving drama school, I landed the part of Forsythe. So my first big role took me into the army as a lieutenant fresh from Sandhurst, precisely the rank and path which my father had envisaged for me! He couldn't believe it and burst out laughing, particularly when I had to have my hair cut short.'

In truth, Ben's family background veered as much towards the theatre as it did the military. 'My great-aunt acted with the likes of Olivier, Noël Coward and Kenneth More; my great-grandmother was an opera singer, and my grandmother was instrumental in bringing the Charleston to England. But they tended to keep the artistic side of the family quiet so that I'd get a proper job in the army.'

Ben trod the boards from an early age. 'At three, I was an angel with a coathanger down my back in a nativity play, and at six I was a cripple with a broom under my arm in a production of *The Pied Piper of Hamelin* at Exeter Cathedral.'

Having decided that his future did not lie with the army after all, he pursued acting with a vengeance and studied at The Drama Centre for six years. After small parts in *The Bill* and *Between the Lines*, he struck gold with *Soldier, Soldier.*

He remembers: 'When I auditioned, I had shoulder-length hair but, in an attempt to look the part, I wore slacks and a military blazer. I talked about my father and I think that must have impressed them. I was in a phone box in Islington High Street when they told me I'd be on the beach in Cyprus in two days. It was like a dream come true.

Ben was only too aware that there would be no shortage of critics if his portrayal of Forsythe lacked credibility. 'I knew I had to be spot on because my father would be watching and if I'd got it wrong, he'd have roasted me. So I said to Dave Attwood, our military advisor: "For Christ's sake, tell me if I'm doing anything wrong or I'll get lynched."'

Fortunately, Ben's only slip-ups have been off-screen or re-shot. 'We did the beach landings in Cyprus at six o'clock in the morning and it was cold and wet. I was the only actor on board the boat – all the rest were extras supplied by the RAF and the army. I said to the others, "Let's do it in one take so that we can get in to the warm." When we came to do it, I leapt off the boat, didn't allow for the weight of the equipment on my back and fell face first in the sea. To make matters worse, everybody else was perfect. We had to do it three times in all.

'Then, right at the end of last series, I dislocated my shoulder in a charity football match between the cast and the crew and the Sergeants' Mess of King's Regiment at Hounslow Barracks. It was agony – it took three people to put my shoulder back into place. Luckily, we had finished filming all of the physical stuff so for the remaining scenes, I just held myself gingerly.'

Ben has now fully recovered and is pleased to report that the show has a new fan – his father. 'He had never watched *Soldier, Soldier* before but now he's hooked. He thinks it's very good military-wise.' For Ben Nealon, the accolades do not come any higher.

Ben Nealon as Lt Jeremy Forsythe

ROBSON GREEN
as FUSILIER DAVE TUCKER

Having announced that this will be his last series of *Soldier, Soldier*, Robson Green has no doubts about how he would like to be written out. 'If it was down to me,' he grins, 'Tucker would spontaneously combust! One minute he'd be there and the next ... whoosh! Lovely!'

Despite his departure, Robson has nothing but fond memories of the series. 'I'm leaving because I think I've taken Tucker as far as I could but I look back on *Soldier, Soldier* with great fondness. I've learned so much, particularly from the way Jerome Flynn times his dialogue. He's had the biggest influence on my acting career. And this fifth series has been terrific, going off to Australia and South Africa. In South Africa, we did an episode about poaching so we were in amongst all the animals. It was something I'd always dreamed of doing. I really do have to pinch myself sometimes to make sure it's all happening to me. I can't believe how lucky I've been.'

Latterly, Robson's good fortune has extended to a musical career. 'Again, it's the childhood thing – acting out my dreams – like a nine-year-old in front of the mirror with a brush. Jerome and I have always driven everyone bananas singing between takes but it was producer Annie Tricklebank who had the idea for us to sing 'Unchained Melody' on the show. We were very apprehensive at first. I was worried about the credibility of a scallywag fusilier singing this song in an angelic way. We decided the only way to approach it was with honesty and sincerity, and it worked. I am proud to say we did it in one take and apparently after the episode was screened, the phone lines were jammed with people wanting to know whether they could buy it on record. Then record companies kept phoning us. It was a bit of a joke at the start but Jerome and I discussed it, and said as long as we had creative control, OK. The

next thing I knew we were doing *Surprise! Surprise!* Just before we sang, I announced, "I've never done this before." And a woman in the audience called out, "Don't worry, love. We're right behind you." That made me feel good.'

In truth, Robson is no stranger to singing. 'When I worked in the shipyards, I sang in an accapella group called The Workey Tickets – in Newcastle if you're a "workey ticket", you're a cheeky little bugger! We raised money for the Durham miners' families during the 1984–85 strike and graduated to singing at the Albert Hall where we supported The Flying Pickets. Then acting came along ...'

At thirty-one, fresh from his success in Catherine Cookson's *The Gambling Man* and happily married to Alison, Robson's life is in stark contrast to Dave Tucker's. 'The Tuckers are going through more turmoil than ever,' says Robson. 'In the first episode of the new series, Macaulay is taken into care after Donna is falsely accused of hitting him. The only way Dave and Donna can get him back is to discover who's really been hitting him and to prove to the courts that they can sustain a relationship that looks comfortable for a child to live in. So Dave and Donna are living in the same house but in separate rooms and that creates issues of loneliness and sexual denial which are tough for him because he loves her. But when it comes to the crunch, I think he loves Macaulay more because he created him. That's what he said: the only thing he ever got right was Macaulay.'

Immediately after filming his final episode of *Soldier, Soldier*, Robson is doing a show at the Live Theatre Company, Newcastle, the place where he made his professional acting debut. 'Hopefully, I can put a few bums on seats and return a little of what they gave me back in July '86. It's my way of saying thank you.'

Robson Green as Fusilier Dave Tucker

SOPHIE DIX
as CAPTAIN SADIE WILLIAMS

Sophie Dix found the role of army doctor Sadie Williams to be a baptism of fire. 'I'd never played a doctor before and my medical knowledge was minimal. But out in Australia, I was taught the basics by a terrific army doctor. Within two minutes of meeting him, I was snapping adrenalin bottles and syringes.

'I quickly found out that being an army doctor is totally different to any other branch of medicine. There's no time for pussyfooting – they can't be precious. It's very hands-on, all mucking in together. They have to work in such unusual surroundings, like the bush and the desert, that they simply have to roll their sleeves up and get on with it. There's no time to stand still in the army.

'For my research, I explored the cases which were coming up but mixed the textbook approach with the requirements of the army. The end result was a long way from *Doctor Finlay!*'

Like Sophie, Sadie Williams was thrown in at the deep end in Australia. 'She had always wanted to be a doctor,' says Sophie, 'but Australia really was new territory for her. Yet she took it all in her stride: she's very calm, cool and committed. Because everyone had to muck in, it helped her establish a bond with the boys. She enjoys a laugh and a joke with them and is able to forget about rank.'

Sadie Williams is twenty-eight. She faced a huge dilemma when her dad was made redundant just before she did her 'A' Levels, which meant that her parents could no longer afford to put her through medical school. Even with a college grant, she would have struggled so she decided to join the Army Medical Corps.

'It's fun playing a bright girl like Sadie,' adds Sophie whose TV credits include *Seconds Out, Between the Lines, The Buccaneers* and *The Devil's Advocate.* 'I've often played extreme roles, sometimes on the wrong side of the law. For example in an episode of *The Bill*, I played a girl who ran over her best mate. But recently I've played a cop in *Thieftakers* and now this. Maybe I'm perceived as having grown up now.

'Going to Australia was a real bonus. I grew up in Devon so I love sun, sea and surf. The only problems were the heat and the flies. The heat was very intense while the flies were a real nuisance. They kept clinging to my eyelashes, my lips and my hair.

'But I'm pleased to say I did see some kangaroos. A group of us drove back in the dark from Ayers Rock and there are all these signs saying: "Beware of camels and kangaroos". We were lucky – we saw kangaroos and emus. Also, the desert flooded while we were there. That's something which only happens every twenty years so, all in all, we felt quite privileged.'

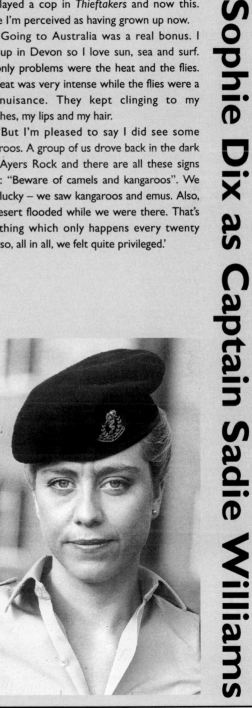

Sophie Dix as Captain Sadie Williams

DOUGRAY SCOTT
as MAJOR RORY TAYLOR

Dougray Scott's only previous military experience was on horseback in period costume. Nevertheless, it provided the Fife-born actor with valuable grounding for his portrayal of Major Rory Taylor.

'I played the Prince Regent's Equerry in the film *Princess Caraboo* and met some of the Household Cavalry who appeared as extras. I became quite friendly with a few of the officers and was able to base certain aspects of Taylor on them.

'Taylor is different to most men of his rank. Although a Sandhurst graduate, he comes from a working-class background and doesn't always behave like an officer. At thirty-two, he has been divorced for two years and out in Australia has a fling with a local girl. Even so, he's a good soldier – tough but fair.'

At one stage, Dougray himself briefly contemplated a career in the services. 'As a boy I wanted to play soccer for Hibs [Hibernian] but then, when I was fifteen, I did think about joining the Navy. I was actually quite close to joining up but then school plays lured me towards acting instead. It was probably just as well. I think my family's politics might have been a little too left-wing for the Navy!'

After training at the Welsh College of Music and Drama, where he won the Most Promising Drama Student award, Dougray progressed to theatre and television. His TV credits include the *Taggart* story 'Nest of Vipers' (in which he played a particularly unpleasant killer), *Lovejoy*, *Stay Lucky* and *Kavanagh, QC*. He also played Don Pedro in a production of *Zorro* for Spanish TV.

'I went to Madrid for that,' says Dougray, 'and then of course there was Australia and South Africa on *Soldier, Soldier*. It was my first time in Australia and I loved it. Sydney was great – really exciting – while Alice Springs was different from anywhere else I've ever been. And I managed to find time to visit the Blue Mountains where an aunt of mine used to live for years.

'I'd been warned about the Australian wildlife but an Aborigine in Alice Springs told me he'd only seen two snakes in twenty years. Perhaps he was trying to make me feel good because Robson and Jerome said they'd seen two deadly taipans in the space of a couple of days!'

Dougray Scott as Major Rory Taylor

ROB SPENDLOVE
as LT MICHAEL STUBBS

When Michael Stubbs was diagnosed as suffering from post traumatic stress disorder in the wake of the tour of duty to Bosnia, Rob Spendlove set out to discover as much about the condition as he could.

'I did a lot of research on PTS,' says forty-two-year-old Rob. 'I talked to an army psychologist who dealt with PTS, and when we got to Germany last year, some of the Coldstream boys, at whose barracks we were based, had just come back from Bosnia so I was able to talk to them. Some had fairly horrific stories and it was interesting to see the different ways in which people were affected. You tend to think stress only happens to the lower ranks but it hits people higher up too. They take a lot on themselves in terms of responsibility.

'Stubbs couldn't understand why a man like him should be suffering from stress. Then he learned that people like Tucker were also affected by it but laughing was their way of getting through a very unpleasant job. It can be a slow-burning condition. One man I heard about got PTS after being in Northern Ireland, and he was affected four years after he came out of the army.'

At the start of the fifth series, Stubbs is promoted to lieutenant. 'Michael has no doubts about his ability in the new rank,' says Rob, 'because he thinks he can do any job in the army better than anyone else. So he rises to it well. But sometimes he's a bit over-zealous – not quite as prepared as he thinks he is – and he has to face the consequences. But he doesn't see them as a personal setback.

'Michael doesn't have many friends though. People tend to keep their distance from him, even his fellow officers. He does have a bit of a bark on him. A lot of the officers he'll meet have been trained by him in the past and he knows that most of them are useless. But he'll enjoy sorting them out: he's an uncomplicated sort of guy.'

Stubbs' home life is destined for further upheavals, however. His new rank causes some friction with Marsha who doesn't always behave like an officer's wife. 'She's a funny old sort,' laughs Rob, 'not the easiest person. So Michael's been through the mill a bit. Even when he was a sergeant major, he wasn't that keen on her mucking about with squaddies' wives, and he's even less keen now. She has to be a bit more careful now and she's not. She's still got this wild side to her.'

Over the years, Rob has specialised in playing shady characters such as Heather's errant husband Roger in *Brookside* and, more recently, a devious councillor in *The Choir*. 'At first glance, you'd think Michael was like that too,' says Rob, 'but in fact he's just straight down the line. He's probably one of the nicest blokes I've played. Mind you, I do enjoy playing shifty characters ...'

Rob Spendlove as Lt Michael Stubbs

DENISE WELCH
as MARSHA STUBBS

Unlike Marsha Stubbs, Denise Welch is over-joyed at Michael's promotion – because it helps her get out of the kitchen.

'I was getting fed up with all those 'who wants a tuna sandwich?' scenes in the kitchen,' laughs Denise. 'It was the same when I was Jimmy Nail's wife in *Spender* – I was always stuck in the kitchen. It was the bane of my life. But now that the kids are not around and Michael's an officer, I've got time to get out more and mix with the girls. And his new rank means that at least I've got a bigger kitchen in which to make tuna sandwiches should they be required!'

Denise is happy to report that Marsha's new status as an officer's wife has also seen improvements in her wardrobe. 'I was promised I wouldn't have to wear leggings and a T-shirt at all in this whole series. Rosie Rowell and I had decided it was becoming a leggings and T-shirt show! So I've been shopping with the wardrobe people to give Marsha a much chicer image.

'As a result, my hair has changed yet again. For the first series it was quite long, for the second it was very short and very white blonde; now, because I'm an officer's wife, I have to conform so it's a bit longer and a bit darker. Some people find it very confusing. They say, "Why do they keep getting different actresses to play Marsha?"

'Marsha has had a very traumatic life but she's managed to survive. Everyone around her seems to have had a nervous breakdown at one time or another but she holds firm. She's very strong and has always been helped by the fact

that she's had a strong marriage. But when Michael wants her to mix more with officers' wives, she finds it hard to give up her squaddie friends. He wants her to play bridge but she doesn't want all that. Michael has had so many run-ins with the Tuckers that he thinks they're trouble and tells Marsha to keep away from Donna. But she likes Donna and Colette, so things get pretty tense at home.'

When this series of *Soldier, Soldier* finishes, Denise is performing an Alan Plater play with husband Tim Healy at the Theatre Royal, Newcastle. 'I don't like leaving our six-year-old son Matthew for long,' says Denise, 'so I'll only do theatre if it's up in the north-east where we live. Fortunately, while I've been doing this latest series of *Soldier, Soldier*, Tim has been at home working on new projects. So he's been able to look after Matthew when I haven't been able to get back.

'Matthew actually came out to Cyprus when we were filming *Soldier, Soldier* there and twice acted as an extra. We don't want him to go into acting as a career but it was fun for him. At least it should have been, but both of his appearances were edited out. On one occasion, he was building a sand castle in a scene behind Rosie Rowell but the way it was edited, they just couldn't keep him in it. All that could be seen on screen was his arm. He was absolutely devastated. He got all his friends round and kept replaying it on the video, just to see his right arm building this sand castle! So we've promised him that if we can get him in as an extra this series, he definitely won't be edited out.'

Denise Welch as Marsha Stubbs

ANNABELLE APSION
as JOY WILTON

Annabelle Apsion is hoping that happier times are around the corner for long-suffering Joy Wilton ... if only so that Annabelle's father can be left in peace.

'Poor Joy, she's had such a miserable time of it,' sighs Annabelle. 'First there was the baby snatch and then Tony's death. Her life has been so full of melodrama that at one stage in the last series, it seemed as if something dreadful was happening to her almost every episode. After Tony died, my dad was in a shop and a woman, who knew he was my father, simply ran out in tears. She was so upset at what had happened to Joy.

'People are forever confusing me with Joy. After the funeral, they came up to me in the street and said what dignity I showed. Not Joy, me! And when I've been doing plays at places like the National, schoolgirls in the audience would always come and ask me, "How's Tone?"

'The thing is that people genuinely seem to like Joy. Women tell me that they'd love to see something nice happen to her and how she's their favourite character in the show. That surprises me, because I always think she's so dull!

'But I do like the humour in the character and she is very well meaning – there's not an unkind bone in her body. That's why it seems so unfair that she's been through so much misery. When Tony died, we saw Joy's inner reserve. Up until then, nobody realised she had any.'

Annabelle admits that she does not relish playing traumatic scenes. 'I much prefer the jollier scenes,' she says. 'I find the sad episodes upsetting because, in order to play the part, I have to go through the mill myself. To be convincing, I have to make myself upset by trying to imagine what it must be like to lose a baby or a husband. I must confess I had serious reservations about doing the baby-snatch storyline. I thought it was too sensational and might worry mums with babies – after all, you do have a responsibility to your audience. But then, just after we had finished filming that episode, baby Abbie Humphries was snatched. So, sadly, these things do happen.'

For the second time in *Soldier, Soldier*, Annabelle experienced screen motherhood. 'In the very first episode, I had to be filmed "giving birth" and for the start of the last series, Joy was pregnant again. It's all a bit of a novelty to me because I'm single myself. This last time, the wardrobe department made a special corset stuffed with soft padding. It wasn't too uncomfortable and a lot of the pregnancy took place while the others were off in Cyprus, so I didn't have to do too many scenes wearing it.'

Immediately prior to the fifth series of *Soldier, Soldier*, Annabelle appeared in *The Blue Ball* at the National Theatre, a play which called for a quick-fire sex change. She explains: 'I played two parts: an astronaut and his wife. Switching between scenes from wife to husband meant the quickest change I've ever had to do. I only had five minutes to get into my spacesuit, change wigs, false eyelashes and so on. By the end of the run, I'd got it down to under a minute and a half. Even Joy would have been proud of such organisation ...'

Annabelle Apsion as Joy Wilton